SEX TALK

SEX TALK

MYRON BRENTON

STEIN AND DAY/*Publishers*/NewYork

First published in 1972
Copyright © 1972 by Myron Brenton
Library of Congress Catalog Card No. 72-81607
All rights reserved
Published simultaneously in Canada by Saunders of Toronto, Ltd.
Designed by David Miller
Printed in the United States of America
Stein and Day/*Publishers*/7 East 48 Street, New York, N.Y. 10017
ISBN 0-8128-1423-1

SECOND PRINTING, 1972

To my friend

Oscar Rabinowitz

Contents

Acknowledgments

It's always a pleasure for a writer to thank his interviewees, the people who give freely of their time and thoughts to help him with his work. Of the experts listed below, most were interviewed directly for this book. I saw a few on other, closely related, projects; the insights they gave me also proved valuable in this context.

My thanks to: Dr. Ruth Aaron, psychoanalyst; Lucile Cantoni of the Family Service of Metropolitan Detroit; Dr. Israel Charny, clinical psychologist; Dr. Philip M. Feldman of the Marriage Council of Philadelphia; Marilyn A. Fithian of the Center for Marital and Sexual Studies; Dr. Gerald I. Gingrich of the Institute for Family Life and Sex Education; Dr. William E. Hartman of the Center for Marital and Sexual Studies; Dr. James L. Hawkins of Indiana University–Purdue University Medical Center; Dr. Warren L. Jones, psychoanalyst; Dr. Sander M. Latts of the University of Minnesota.

And to: Dr. Arnold A. Lazarus of Yale University; Dr. Gregory T. Leville of the Family Service of Philadelphia; Dr. Stanley R. Lesser, child psychiatrist; Dr. Harold Lief of the Marriage Council of Philadelphia; Dr. Eleanor B. Luckey of the University of Connecticut; Dr. Judd Marmor of Cedars-Sinai

Medical Center; Sherod Miller of the University of Minnesota; Dr. Gerhard Neubeck of the University of Minnesota; Dr. David M. Reed of the Marriage Council of Philadelphia; Drs. Philip and Lorna Sarrel of Yale University; Robert Sunley of the Family Service Association of Nassau County; Dr. Alan J. Wabrek of the University of Pennsylvania.

I also interviewed nearly four dozen nonprofessionals, men and women who were willing to talk with me about their personal lives—their successful and unsuccessful attempts at sex talk with sex partners and children, their sexual fantasies, experiences, and problems. Our understanding was that they would remain anonymous. So they shall, but my gratitude to them all.

During the course of my research I attended and took part in UNITE, a communications course for engaged and married couples given by the Family and Children's Service in Minneapolis, Minn. The course was extremely rewarding to me both personally and professionally; what's more, it resulted in friendships with four people whose expertise has helped to make the book better and whose warmth has made my life richer. And so I'd like to give special thanks to Earl Beatt, Ron Brazman, Barbara McLane, and Ann Wiens—all from the Family and Children's Service, all UNITE co-leaders.

My thanks, too, to Lennie Gross for various and sundry favors rendered in connection with this book.

Needless to say, the construction of the book and its overall points of view are my own—and my own responsibility entirely.

1

Why It's Hard to Talk Sex

SEXUAL ILLITERACY

This is a book about sex talk—about the ways we communicate sexually; about the hidden sexual messages we send to our spouses, lovers, or children; about the ease with which attempts at honest sexual discussions often flounder; and about the techniques we can employ to be more skillful and effective in talking sex.

No question about it, we've become more open and expressive about sex than would have been deemed possible even a scant decade ago. Especially in public we speak with remarkable candor; at least, the culture as a whole does. X-rated movies, best-selling erotic fiction and manuals on sensuality, the publicity being given to sex research and therapy, the debates on sexual politics—all attest to the way we're using sex words and words about sex.

Yet a paradox exists. For all the talk about sex, many of us are still sexual illiterates, particularly in the conduct of our private lives. Yes, we snap up books on being more sensual and accomplished in bed. But the ability to talk with genuine

15

candor and openness about sex—an ability basic to accomplishment—is given to few.

Most of us find it hard to talk in depth about sex even with
those persons with whom we're closest and most intimate. It is
still far easier to ask somebody to go to the movies than to go
to bed. Easier to exchange feelings about music, politics, child-
rearing—about almost anything—than about sex. Easier to discuss what we'd like for dinner than what we'd like to do and
have done to us sexually. Easier to talk over what went right or
wrong with a party we just gave than what went right or wrong
with a sexual experience we've just had. Easier to speak with
our children about money, clothes, hair, drugs, than to speak
with them about sex.

This is a pity because the less we know how to talk about
sex, the more a hit-or-miss proposition our sex lives are likely to
be. Conversely, the greater our ability to express ourselves
about sex, the greater the likelihood that we will be bettering or
enriching our sexual experiences *and* the relationships from
which they spring; of raising our children to be sexually secure
and mature adults; of successfully concluding, rather than in-
advertently short-circuiting, the sexual transactions of our lives.

Once you've mastered the skills involved in sexual communication, you can:

—Develop a clearer knowledge of what your sexual values
are, since knowing where you're at sexually is basic to talking
honestly about sex.

—Gain insight into how you and others communicate sexually by the way you conduct your sex lives and by the ways
you make love.

—Pinpoint communications traps that lead to sexual and
emotional conflict.

—Talk with your sex partner about the most sensitive,
potentially explosive facets of your sex lives.

—Correctly interpret your children's sexual remarks—and
reach them in terms of sexual guidance.

—Read the signs that tell you when to avoid talking to a friend or professional about sex.

Such skills are the stuff of "literacy" in sexual communication. It's what the ensuing chapters will deal with.

THE POWER OF THE WORDS

In some progressive classes in human sexuality given at universities, sex language isn't ignored and, as a result, interesting things happen. Dr. Gerhard Neubeck, who teaches a popular class of this kind at the University of Minnesota, knows that before students can get down to sex concepts they have to get over vocabulary hangups. So these young men and women—the latest products of the sexual revolution, the ones most hip about sex—face each other fully and, eyes locked, say the loaded words: penis, vagina, erection . . . And the more explosive four letter words as well.

The interesting thing is the way these students initially react. They giggle. They blush. They laugh nervously. In sum, they show a good deal of anxiety. Sex words still are a threat, even for students who elect to take a course on human sexuality.

"To talk sex," says Dr. Neubeck, "is still to be a sinner."

Not only sex words themselves but words about sex are loaded ones. This is often brought out at the Center for Marital and Sexual Studies in Long Beach, California. The Center is a nonprofit organization devoted to sex research and therapy. Some couples go there because they want help with problems related to orgasmic dysfunction; others go because they volunteer themselves as research subjects much as happens at the famed Masters-Johnson clinic in St. Louis.

Obviously, such volunteer couples are much less inhibited then most of us are, can be—or, perhaps, want to be. They know beforehand they'll be asked to engage in sexual intercourse in a special little chamber where they'll be clinically monitored and tape recorded. They welcome this kind of scientific observation. Yet, they are sexually tongue-tied.

Dr. William E. Hartman, director of the Center, explains, "Most of the time these couples sound as though they're in a mausoleum. Nobody tells anybody anything, what they're thinking, what they're feeling. Occasionally a girl says, 'This is really good, I'm enjoying it, you're very sensitive,' but that's all."

According to other sexologists and nonprofessionals in various parts of the country, these volunteer couples pretty much exemplify most of us. Many couples tend to be as quiet while making love as if engaged in illicit activity. With some, hushed moans, groans, and whispers, maybe a muffled "Higher, Harry" or "Did you, Clara?" represents the full flowering of sex-act sex talk. Relatively few are any more explicit, tell each other what they want and they feel, scream out words and phrases that have an aphrodisiac effect on themselves and their partners. Sex is still the great taboo and the way in which most people contain themselves while having sex shows it.

"I want to shout all the four-letter words I know," one middle-aged man told me, "but then somehow I just don't have the guts. I don't know what kind of a reaction I'll get from my wife and the idea of doing it embarrasses even me."

Ironically, I've heard this same man, in a fit of anger, tell somebody, "Go fuck yourself!" "Fuck" is much more often used as a word of hostility than of arousal.

WHERE IT ALL BEGINS

There are two main reasons why it's hard to talk sex. One has to do with early associations between sex and sex talk, the other with the risky nature of sex talk. Think first about how children typically grow up: as toddlers they're usually given euphemisms only for the genitals, the process of birth, and elimination. This makes its impact later on when real names are substituted. The youngster can't help but wonder: What's so different about these parts of the body and these activities? Why were they singled out?

Youngsters—very young ones as well as those "middle-aged" and older—masturbate. Most parents, directly or indirectly, at the very least communicate their lack of ease about it. The children's body of knowledge grows: sex is not only different, it's nasty. (Where sex therapy is now available on campus to college students, as at the University of Pennsylvania, Yale, North Carolina, and about a dozen more schools, one problem students often bring to counselors is guilt over masturbation. This may astonish some people who believe the sexual revolution has swept the young fully in its tide.)

More signals of the same sort: children bring home and proudly display their first "dirty" words; they quickly learn that these are bad. Their sexual curiosity, confusion, anxieties, and fantasies are augmented when their parents engage in a practice Dr. John G. Gagnon has called "mislabeling"—seeing sex in words and activities that aren't sexual at all from the child's point of view. "Nonlabeling" also has its effect—the practice of conspicuously *not* talking about sex and not giving the child a "meaningful vocabulary with which to communicate or to elicit information"; this "creates a zone of the body about which there is some fundamental mystery and concern." Then there's the matter of no-no's: a very young child's life is filled with prohibitions—crossing the street, playing with matches, and so on; in time all are methodically revised or removed—except, often, those having to do with sex. Sex then remains a topic dealt with largely in negatives, especially for girls.

So children learn that sex and references to sex stir up flurries of emotion. They learn to snigger about sex with friends, swapping the prohibited terms, trading information and misinformation, using sex words as angry words just as they've heard their parents do. (I wonder what would happen if parents avoided that practice and universally said something along the lines of, "Look, these are wonderful words. They describe beautiful things and actions. I don't want you to spoil them by saying them just for the sake of saying them or when you're angry at somebody. Later on you'll be using them in an important and lovely way, as special grown-up words of love.")

The children grow older, catch on to dirty jokes, trade these with friends, and discover that just *talking* about sex can make them feel funny. (Pubescent boys not infrequently have erections when they hear sex jokes.) It's an important discovery, too, for now there's the realization that sex talk can be truly powerful—not only because it produces guilt but also because it produces vivid sexual fantasies, vivid enough to bring on desire. Pornography derives its power, after all, from the unique effect of sex words and descriptions—they practically compel us to visualize what's being described.

So children reach adolescence without having learned to handle sex talk easily, especially the many children who haven't had a history of good sexual communication at home or been exposed to effective sex education courses. Sex talk with parents drops off markedly. When dating, most teenagers don't—can't—ask their dates the questions they want to ask: about sexual feelings and reactions, about what pleases them and turns them off, about the meaning that sex has for them, about contraception. Kids talk about things more openly than ever, but much adolescent sex talk is "surface" talk. The high rate of unwanted pregnancies among teenage girls, the appalling lack of sexual knowledge about themselves and each other that boys and girls display in high school and college, the eagerness with which they embrace classes and services having to do with sex—all such phenomena prove it. Many teenagers still don't come to grips with the issues that are important to them. They haven't learned how. They've learned, as we all have to some degree or other, that sex talk is dirty talk, dangerous talk.

SEX AND RISK

Sex talk is dangerous talk too because it's emotional. It's emotional talk not only because of guilt but also because of risk. To verbalize anything is to expose it, transform it from something private into something public. Once it's public it's open to judgment, to criticism. More precisely, when we're open with respect to our sexual feelings and wishes, *we're* open to judgment, to criticism, to put-downs, to rejection.

This holds true for any sensitive aspect of our lives, of course, but all the more so for sex. Why? Because for many of us in our culture so much of our sense of ourselves is tied up with sex. With sexual attractiveness, sexual identity, sexual capacity, sexual performance, sexual morality, sexual something or other. Such things have much to do with our images of ourselves, with our worth as masculine and feminine beings. When it comes to sex, image may not be all, but in our culture it's at least as substantial as the penis and the vagina.

On some sexual scale, modest or otherwise, we need to be winners: need to be desired, possessed of the ability to give and receive pleasure, normal (whatever that means to us individually). It follows that the more open we are, and the more we reveal of ourselves, the greater the risk that we won't seem to be so winning to others. As a consequence, even people who are glib, smooth talkers with regard to some facets of sex clam up with regard to other facets.

Ellen is an example. Ellen is a young wife who fancies herself cool about sex. She and her husband have done a lot of sexual experimenting. Yet there was one thing she always wanted to try and never could bring herself to voice—anal intercourse. Somehow the idea of suggesting that particular technique overwhelmed her; she thought if she did the proverbial roof would fall in.

Eventually, Ellen saw a social worker for several sessions on another problem, a problem related to one of her children, and eventually her sex life became a subject for discussion. Because Ellen found the social worker enormously sympathetic, she opened up. She mentioned her secret wish, half expecting the woman to be shocked.

"Haven't you ever discussed it with your husband?" asked the social worker.

"Well, I almost did once or twice," said Ellen. "But somehow I could never quite get the words out."

"Why not?"

"Because he'd probably think me awful," she replied.

Following that session Ellen did suggest anal intercourse to her husband, probably because the social worker's reaction had been so matter-of-fact. He didn't fall apart, either. They tried it. As it turned out, neither of them really enjoyed anal intercourse, but that's not the point. The point is that Ellen thought her husband would be revolted by her if she suggested it, so for the longest time she wouldn't take the chance. Many people are like Ellen. They find it easy to talk about some things but there are other things they find overwhelming because of their own feelings about them, and so they can't "quite get the words out."

What's safe to talk about? What's risky? Clearly this is an individual matter; what may upset one person another may remark upon as easily as upon the weather. Still, some generalizations can be made. In the considerable experience of Dr. Philip M. Feldman of the Marriage Council of Philadelphia, the second oldest and the most prestigious institution of its kind in the nation, sex partners are most likely to risk talking to each other about:

—Conventional sex and sex techniques.

—Conventional sex problems like impotence and frigidity (probably because of the widespread publicity the Masters-Johnson research in sex therapy has been getting).

—Dissatisfactions with the frequency of sex relations.

Conversely, sex partners are more likely to have difficulty talking about:

—A wish for any unconventional sex practice which can be interpreted as perverse or abnormal by those who feel insecure about it. Despite their current popularity both fellatio and cunnilingus must be counted among these; anal sex, of course; harmless little quirks like wanting a big toe sucked, as well as outrageous fetishes; and, for the more timid, some of the more imaginative sex positions.

—A wish for passive sex, simply wanting to be masturbated on a particular occasion rather than engaging in standard, reciprocal sex.

—A wish for aggressive sex; wanting to bite, scratch, moan, scream, yell sex words, really let go and have the partner let go.

—A wish to have emotional needs satisfied—for instance, to be held, or to be told how sexually stimulating one is, or to be told how marvelous one is in bed.

—A wish to air grievances that are apt to cause anger and pain in one's partner.

Risk is related to trust, and trust is related to what kind of a relationship a couple has overall. Logically, the more open their total relationship, the more likely the two partners are to be free and open about sex. But people don't always behave according to logic. Some couples are free about everything— except about sex. Some have a rotten relationship and lousy communication—except in bed; there, figuratively, they babble on as spontaneously as carefree kids—for a time, at least. Even couples who swing can be shy about sex—at any rate, about emotional factors related to sex. Swingers often get a lot of pleasure comparing notes with their mates about what they did with whom. But there are swinging husbands and wives who no longer enjoy swinging, who want something that's emotionally more rewarding, but find that hard to admit to their mates.

Ultimately, trust turns on oneself. The surer we are about

ourselves, and the more confident we are about the things we think and say, the more we can trust ourselves to say them. Self-confidence is related to a number of factors, of course, but communication is one of them. An awareness of how we communicate sexually can provide strengthening insights. Understanding and applying the principles of sexual communication can do much to help overcome inhibitions and start the opening-up process that leads to growing pleasure and greater intimacy.

The Ways
You
Talk Sex

2

But What's Going On Underneath?

SEX TALK—HERE, THERE, EVERYWHERE

We don't talk sex with talk alone. Words count for a great deal, of course. But so do looks, tones, actions, gestures, the personalities we project, the lives we lead. In a broad sense everything we do is related to sex: it reflects our total self, which includes the sexual dimension.

In this sense, even clothes, hobbies, and occupations say something sexual. Often the message is very subtle, but sometimes it is quite clear. One man I know never puts on short-sleeved shirts, even on the hottest days of summer, because he has thin arms and displaying them would make him feel less manly. Another acquaintance, a middle-aged divorced man, has taken to wearing very tight jeans because "all the available women glance at my crotch and it turns them on—they know it, I know it." His tight-fitting jeans proclaim something about himself: "I've got it and I want to show it off."

A few years ago Dr. D. W. Heyder and a colleague from the Norfolk Mental Health Center took a close psychological look at Navy frogmen. In the stereotype, frogmen are really masculine figures because their training and work requires them to withstand tremendous amounts of physical and emotional stress. But when the researchers compared trainees who couldn't stand the gaff and dropped out of training with those who gritted their teeth and made it, they discovered something about the latter group. These successful trainees, unlike the dropouts, tended to fear women and doubt their sexual adequacy.

"It is quite possible," the researchers suggested, "that their unconscious motivation to complete the course was based on a need to prove their masculinity coupled with a fear of involvement with women."

The point is that sex talk occurs all around us, even under water.

We needn't, shouldn't, and can't analyze everything we do for its sexual content. We're not trained for the job, there's little profit in it on an amateur basis, and, most important, such preoccupation would drain any pleasure from life. Nevertheless, it is good to bear in mind that sex "talk" is many-faceted.

Most significantly, the quality of our interpersonal relationships carries potent sexual messages. Men and women who are generally tender, loving, passive, timid, competitive, or domineering with each other are most apt to be tender, loving, passive, timid, competitive, or domineering in the bedroom, too. Mothers and fathers teach their children at least as much about sexual relationships by their day-to-day interaction as they do by strict sex education. People who fear warmth and closeness in their social or family relationships are also most apt to be cold or distant in their sexual relationships. Socially and sexually we're of a piece.

BODY TALK AND OTHER SIGNALS

Body talk—nonverbal communication—has gotten a good

deal of clinical and popular attention lately. Tone of voice, look of eye, stance, gestures, touches, caresses (as well as not touching, not caressing), changes in breathing—all are elements of it. This form of talk can be eloquent indeed in its capacity to confirm or contradict one's spoken words. The very term "body talk" suggests its importance in sexual communication; in fact, as Chapter 5 will show, the way we use our bodies in sex is a specific form of sexual communication all its own.

Sometimes body talk is forcefully direct, as when, locked in a sexual embrace, a woman kneads her lover's back with her fingers in rhythm to her rising sexual beat, faster and faster, until she reacher orgasm. "This is the tempo," those fingers say, "at which I want to receive your thrusts." And they also say, "I'm coming along, coming along, coming along."

Sometimes body talk is less blunt. An example is what Dr. Albert E. Scheflen of the Albert Einstein College of Medicine has called "courtship behavior." This is unconscious preening behavior that occurs when men and women are attracted to each other. The man is apt to comb his hair, fiddle with his tie, pull up his socks. The woman is apt to stroke her hair, glance at herself in the mirror, fuss with her clothing.

Either sex is apt to send all kinds of quick little signals to the other; it's not hard to translate them into words. When she's with a male she finds attractive a woman may give him a quick, flashing glance ("hey, sexy!"), cross or uncross her legs ("look, look"), smooth her hand over her skirt ("there are wonders beneath"), arch her back to bring her breasts into greater prominence ("see what I've got").

Sometimes body talk is really a collection of subtle nuances, nothing very concrete, that nevertheless add up to a fairly powerful message. One day a couple married for twenty-five years came to the Marriage Council in part because they were having increasing sexual problems. The wife, the complainant in this case, accused her husband of being sexually inhibited. It wasn't so much the frequency as the quality of sex that disturbed her; her mate just didn't throw himself into sex with the vigor she claimed she wanted.

Everything she said was true enough—but in time the counselor on the case pieced together a more complicated tale. The facts? The husband actually wanted to be more aggressive, to bite and scratch. These were the signals he sent out. Subliminally his wife picked them up; she *sensed* that he wanted to let go. Well, wasn't that what she wanted too? Yes and no. Consciously, yes—but underneath the surface she was frightened of sexual aggression and therefore used her own kind of body talk. By her expressions, by the way she held him when they had sex, by the way her muscles tensed, by a host of such things, she signaled him *not* to be aggressive. Since basically he was a passive sort, he complied.

When all this surfaced the counselor could explore the situation with them and finally they did become more vigorous in their lovemaking. The truly remarkable thing is that for twenty-five years they'd carried on a wordless exchange that went something like this:

He: Hey, I really want to let go.

She: No, don't.

He: Okay.

Remarkable—but by no means unusual. In fact, somewhat the same problem that beset this couple often occurs in reverse, with similar signals flitting back and forth. The scenario goes something like this: a husband complains that his wife isn't as sexually responsive as he'd like her to be. Underneath he really doesn't want her too responsive because then she might turn out to be too much for him—make sexual demands he couldn't meet, perhaps, or leave him for a more virile man. So he sends her wordless signals that say, "Be a little shy, don't be too aggressive sexually." And this is what she picks up and this is what she heeds. The pattern is very familiar to therapists and marriage counselors.

SEX—THE GREAT KIDDER

As such cases show, we're very prone to fool ourselves in terms of our sexual selves. This is most clearly seen in extreme situations: Don Juans often have serious potency problems—which is the reason they keep running from woman to woman, pretending to be great lovers. The most blatant female sexpots not infrequently tighten up in bed, unable to be orgasmic. Some of the most energetic campaigners in the fight against pornography are tormented by crazy sexual fantasies, and some of the people who put on a great show of sexual libertarianism are amazingly narrow-minded when it comes to their own spouses or daughters.

In gross terms, such cases illustrate what, to greater or lesser degree, goes on with all of us. The more investment we have in a particular sexual image, the greater our tendency to fool ourselves or others. There are things we don't want others to see. More important, there are things we ourselves don't want to see. As the Philadelphia Marriage Council's Dr. Feldman says, "People can expound a philosophy of sexuality, but often that's based on a lot of head work—it doesn't relate to their real sexuality."

This doesn't mean it's incumbent upon us to show ourselves psychically naked to the world. Nor does it mean we must inspect every little nook and cranny of our hidden beings. But unless we show some awareness of our sexual selves—of our values, attitudes, and vulnerabilities related to sex—our sexual communications are likely to be confused and contradictory.

Witness Carol and Bill, law students at a prominent Ivy League college. They lived together for six months and in all that time Carol couldn't achieve a single orgasm. The school offers sex therapy through its counseling services, and that's where the two finally went for help.

During their initial counseling session, Carol said to Bill,

"You're putting pressure on me to have an orgasm. I don't think I should be under that kind of pressure."

"I'm not doing that," Bill protested.

"Well, you raised it as an issue first," she pointed out.

"That's because you had other relationships and I thought if you experienced it with other guys I wasn't doing something right. I felt especially sensitive because you'd had prior experience and I hadn't."

"What do you mean, you hadn't?" demanded Carol, genuinely astonished. "What about Jane and Mary and Sally?"

Bill looked startled. "Did I tell you I had sex with those girls?"

"You sure did."

Grinning sheepishly, he confessed, "I was exaggerating a little. I never had intercourse with anyone in my life before I met you."

Carol burst out laughing and said, "Well, the truth is I haven't been all that orgasmic, either."

That session in the counselor's office was the first time they had really ever leveled with each other. It did a lot to help clear the air and get them to relax with each other. Both had been acting out images—he of the stud male, she of the orgiastic female, kidding themselves and each other. Both had felt quite insecure about sex; neither was able to admit this. Instead, unaware, they sent each other oppressive, self-defeating nonverbal messages. "Make me feel like a man," was Bill's. "Make me feel like a woman," was Carol's. The pressure generated by these demands had a destructive effect upon their relationship, sexual and otherwise.

Witness Lorna, mother of a pretty sixteen-year-old, whose own confusions resulted in confusing and destructive communication. The teenager had been born before Lorna and her husband, the girl's father, married. Lorna never really acknowledged to herself the deep shame and guilt she felt about this;

outwardly she shrugged off, with a laugh, the circumstances surrounding her daughter's birth.

But the moment the girl reached pubescence, Lorna's real feelings emerged full force. She became excessively concerned about the child's sexual activities, about the possibility that she might run wild. By her excessive concern she made herself and her daughter miserable. Lorna truly thought she was sending the message, "I worry lest you get into a sexual situation you can't handle." Her real message was, "I worry lest you become promiscuous the way I see myself as having been." In time the girl reacted predictably: she did run wild.

Had Lorna been more aware of her own sexual attitudes, more sensitive to herself, she would probably have done a much better job of communicating with her child. She would have kept her cool. Her concern would have been more balanced and the girl would have been much better able to accept it.

So there it is: we want our words to count, but they'll only do so if other aspects of our behavior don't refute them. That calls for self-awareness. You have to have a pretty good idea of who you are, sexually speaking, before you can do an effective job of speaking sexually.

3

The
Real
Sexual
You

GETTING IN TOUCH WITH YOURSELF

To really get in touch with others sexually you first have to get in touch with yourself sexually. The word "touch" itself is suggestive. Think of "I'm touched." Think of "You touch me deeply." The implication is clear: a wish for physical closeness, physical intimacy—and, in fact, a warm, emotional feeling usually prompts us to such expressions. Now think of "touch" in cold, detached terms: some people are "touchy"—they don't like to be touched; they're closed off emotionally and maybe physically, too.

Dr. Hartman of the Center for Marital and Sexual Studies says, "Getting in touch with yourself is touching yourself symbolically and asking yourself, 'How do I feel?'"

A number of women who seek help at the Center are so out of touch with their own bodies they claim they never have orgasms though clinically they very much do. Sometimes it shocks them to learn the truth about themselves; one patient reacted by starting to have sex with her husband every day. Since she was having climaxes anyway, she figured, she might as well start enjoying them!

Whether you're a woman or a man, there's a set of exercises used at the Center, adapted and modified here, that can help you get in touch with your body. That can help you discover something about yourself in relation to your body.

First: Strip bare. Stand in front of a full-length mirror—a three-way mirror, if possible—under a good light. Relax; make an effort to let tension ooze out.

We tend to take our bodies for granted, as we take for granted the streets and gardens we hurry through, blind to color and detail. But now look, really look, at your body. Look at it as if you're discovering it for the first time. See the curves, the flat and rounded surfaces, the angles, the hair, the texture of the skin, the differing colors and shadings. What pleases you? What disturbs you? Can you voice aloud—or jot down on a sheet of paper—the praiseworthy and the critical things you discover about yourself? Now let your mind roam over your body and your life. Has your body made a difference in the way you've conducted your life?

Second: Run your fingers slowly over your entire body, from head to toe. Explore. You're on a voyage of self-discovery. How do you feel about doing this? Self-conscious? Pleased? Do you feel dulled—feel nothing? Have you ever run your hand lovingly, exploring, over your entire body? If not, why not?

Now, as you do the exercise, does anything feel new and unfamiliar? Where do you linger—or want to linger? Where do you have a tendency to hurry? What thoughts come into your head as you do this exercise? Especially what stray, evanescent thoughts? (If you can catch them, put them on paper—these can be the most meaningful; they're the least censored.)

Third: Now you'll embark on a fantasy tour. Concentrate on your genitals. If you're a woman, place your hand on your vagina and let your imagination go. Fancy yourself sliding along your vaginal lips and climbing into your vagina. If you're a man, touch your penis and testicles, and likewise imagine yourself inside. Give it time. If it helps to close your eyes, close them.

We're not used, most of us, to fantasizing like this. What is it, then, that you see? Nothing? Something strictly anatomical? Or can you soar on great flights of fancy? That is, do inhibitions shut out all images—or do you tend to intellectualize sex—or do you really open up?

Among the people who do this exercise at the Center, women tend to be more sensually inventive than men. They're better able to verbalize color and detail, probably because they're generally brought up to be freer emotionally than are men. One fanciful lady saw her vagina as a "beautiful, soft, velvety place in which butterflies fly around." Among men, engineers tend to give more mechanical presentations than do males in most other professions. A lot of men think small: what emerges from their fantasies is that their penises are a lot smaller than they'd like. One man saw his penis as minuscule— yet the women he had sex with typically complained that it was too big, causing them discomfort!

"PRIMAL" SEX ORGANS

The late Dr. Eric Berne, founder of transactional analysis, called "primal" those images of the vagina that boy children form in their minds and the images of the penis that girl children form in theirs. Images that remain hovering somewhere in the mind of the child turned adult, no matter how old or knowing or experienced that adult may eventually become.

(Berne referred to an obstetrician, a man who has seen hundreds of vaginas in all kinds of conditions and situations, whose internal child nevertheless "still pictured the vagina as an enormous dark bottomless cave in which his penis or even his whole body could get lost.")

Primal or not, we do all have lurking somewhere within us fanciful, revealing images of the opposite-sex sex organs—images that have a bearing on our own view of sex and sex relationships. If you're a woman, think of the male organs—the penis stem and cap, the testicles hanging in their sac of skin. Similarly, if you're a man, think of the female organs—the lips, the clitoris, the vaginal slit surrounded by its pubic brush.

Maybe nothing will come of it the first or second or third time you try; on the other hand, an image may float to the surface when you least expect it.

One woman who did this exercise saw the penis as a big club with little bumps on it, a second saw it as a lollipop, a third as a dueling sword with a bloody tip, a fourth as a scrawny chicken neck she would have "dearly loved to choke." One man saw the vagina as a malodorous swamp, a second as a warm moist little cavern in which he could hide, a third as a scary cave that was booby-trapped with barbs, a fourth as a festering sore, a fifth man saw the clitoris as a darting and caressing little tongue.

The symbolism in each case is evident: the sex organ is something that means pain or comfort; something that hurts or is to be hurt; something to suck, stroke, burrow into, lick, or catch a disease from.

YOUR SEXUAL HISTORY

So there's your body and its genital area—maybe the most dangerous area, maybe the one you're proudest of, maybe the one that's least consequential in your life, maybe the one whose importance you exaggerate. There are the opposite-sex genitals—pleasure-giving, soothing, fearful. Whatever your feelings, the sexual values that you embody result from a multiplicity of life experiences. To examine those experiences takes a different kind of looking and thinking. It also takes a good deal of honesty.

The following questionnaire is based on programs of self-exploration being developed at the University of Minnesota and elsewhere. You can explore your history alone, of course, endeavoring to evoke the sounds and feelings of childhood—or you can do so reciprocally, with someone to whom you're tied by a bond of intimacy. It's in the sharing of memories and emotions with somebody close to one, in sparking each other off, that fresh insights into oneself come easiest and best.

1. How did your parents relate to each other? Children absorb and incorporate what they see. If a son sees his father valuing and respecting his mother and vice versa, he's going to absorb that style and moreover it will help him to grow up thinking, "The sexes are friends; I needn't be afraid." If he grows up seeing a power struggle between his parents, he may think, "You can't trust women farther than you can throw them; be on guard." If his mother is a dominating, possessive woman and his father runs away—possibly by sleeping with other women—or knuckles under, he may believe, "Women have the power to make men weak—to castrate them." If his father dominates his mother, the attitude he'll probably develop is "Women aren't worth much." Girls' attitudes are similarly formed.

What was it like between your parents?

2. How did you grow up feeling about yourself as male or female? When mothers and fathers accept and enjoy their femaleness and maleness they lay the groundwork for their same-sex children to feel, "It's great to be what I am." When they don't—when a father feels bad about himself as a man, when a mother thinks it was a terrible act of fate to have been born a woman—the children become considerably less sure about their own sexual identity. Going further, when a parent even subtly rejects a female child because she's a girl, or a male child because he's a boy, the stage is set for an even greater sense of self-doubt in terms of the child's sexuality.

How did you grow up feeling?

3. What was conveyed to you about relating to the opposite sex? Many women have been brought up in a kind of narcissistic fashion—look pretty, be enticing, don't get sexually involved, keep the guys from taking advantage of you, lead them on to marriage. Many men have been brought up to feel that scoring sexually while avoiding emotional entanglements is the sine qua non of masculinity. This creates a confusing and exploitative atmosphere, one in which women find it difficult to enjoy sex for its own sake and men are reluctant to admit to their emotional needs. Many young people today are deliberately avoiding the exploitative model.

Did you escape the trap?

4. *Did you see either of your parents nude—and, if so, what kind of an impression did it make on you?* The way nudity is handled in the home says a good deal about the sexual atmosphere generated in that home. In one family nudity is an occasional thing, something that occurs naturally and is treated matter-of-factly. In another family a child accidentally wanders into a bedroom where a parent is partially naked and all hell breaks loose—the child is shamed and reprimanded. In a third family a seductive game goes on, usually not calculatedly: a parent often parades around with little or nothing on, oblivious to the way an opposite-sex child (or even a child of the same sex) is stimulated. In a fourth family attempts are made to cover up, but coyly and seductively, so that the child is all the more enticed. There are other variations and all hint at the overall sexual style of the family.

How was nudity handled in your home?

5. *What is your first explicit sexual memory?* For most people it's some kind of superficial sex play with another child, maybe at five or six or so. Whatever the sexual memory is, it can be a natural, developmental phase or an arresting, traumatic experience. One man in his twenties recalls being locked in his bathroom with a little neighborhood girl when he was six years old; they were exploring each other when his mother unexpectedly came home. She hammered on the bathroom door, raged, wouldn't let him see the little girl again. The experience couldn't fail to color his feelings about sex. In some cases one's

first childhood memory of sex is far more wounding—as in the case of a five-year-old girl and her family's gardener; one day he forced her to fondle his penis. The incident left her shaken; in fact, to this day she has difficulty touching even her husband's penis. Such incidents are far from uncommon.

Think back. Was yours an easy or a violent first experience?

6. *How was sex education handled in your home?* When children receive direct, straightforward sex information on their own level of comprehension it lessens—satisfies—their curiosity about sex. Evasion and avoidance create anxiety and arouse curiosity—in effect, they act as stimulants. A more potent form of "education" is involved in what the parents indirectly convey about sex—whether the undertone is one of fear, repugnance, apathy, or joy. How parents handle masturbation also makes a strong impact. A child's attitude toward sex in general and his sex organs in particular is in part formed by the way his parents have dealt with him in terms of masturbation, whether they have made it seem natural or nasty.

How were such things handled in your home?

7. *When did you first learn about sexual intercourse—and what were your feelings about it?* Children generally learn the slang words for sexual intercourse long before they come to realize what intercourse is all about. How they come to realize it can also play an important role in forming their attitudes about sex. A calm, rational description by a stable adult who paints the sex act in natural and wholesome colors can be as reassuring as the often wild, flawed sketches from other children can be unsettling. One man's older sister told him, when he was six, what sex was all about. Cruelly, she embellished the account with warnings to the effect that the penis can be trapped and mutilated inside the vagina. Many years went by before he understood otherwise, and he was well into adulthood before he could really shake his fear altogether.

What was your first learning experience?

8. *What did you absorb about "appropriate" sexual behav-*

ior for men and women? Most people, men and women both, grow up somehow absorbing that the two sexes aren't equal in terms of sexual performance. It's a more insidious sexual double standard even than the one that proclaims that men have sexual rights women don't have—more insidious because it's much less obvious. It makes these assumptions: sex is something men *do* to women; orgasm is something men *have* and *induce* in women; even if they do a lot of thrashing and flailing in bed, women are basically passive during the sex act. In effect, the woman is acted upon, the man does the acting; the onus for performance is on him, while hers is basically a static role.

At Yale University, where courses in human sexuality bear down strongly on the fallacy of this attitude, both boys and girls react with evident relief. Are you relieved, too?

TO THE CORE OF THINGS

Read a filthy paperback novel or go see a really raunchy X-rated movie. You may find it dreadful, or dreadfully boring, but see it through to the end. Then settle down, have a drink, and explore these questions:

1. On the whole, did the book or movie offend, disgust, amuse, excite, or bore you?

2. Was there any part that particularly turned you on?

3. Any part that particularly turned you off?

4. Any part that reminded you of something about yourself you'd rather not have been reminded of?

5. Any part that made you very angry?

6. Any part that made you want to try it?

7. Any character you'd like to have been or played?

This exercise, too, can be done alone or—best—with someone intimate, someone with whom you can really let your psychic hair down. Your reactions may surprise you. You can get a lot out of this one if you let yourself.

THE KICKER

As an extension of that last exercise, explore these questions:

1. What sexual positions, techniques, or acts do you consider truly immoral?

2. Why?

3. What sexual positions, techniques, or acts would you like to engage in but never have?

4. Well, why haven't you?

Remember, the idea behind the exercises in this chapter isn't to engage in a kind of self-therapy. It's to become more self-aware, to communicate more effectively with yourself so that you can talk more effectively with others. The next two chapters, which deal with sexual intercourse itself as a form of communication, may help you further that process.

4

What People Say with Sex

SEX AS SEX TALK

Doreen is twenty-seven, single, insecure, flashy; she comes on strong. She frequents singles bars and organized dances; if she meets a guy who's willing to spend the evening with her and take her home, she's usually willing to sleep with him. She pretends to enjoy sex more than she actually does. "Sex is how you get and keep a man interested in you," is what she believes and communicates. "Sex is what keeps him coming back." And so it does sometimes, at least for a little while.

Mark, in his thirties, also makes the singles scene—bars, cruises, resorts. Mark is the quintessential lonely bachelor; he wants to be emotionally involved but fears commitment. He leads an active sex life, most active when he feels anxious; then he calls up a "regular" girl friend or makes the singles scene. Though he glamorizes his bachelor status, the sex message he sends is, "Make me forget my anxieties, make me feel good, make me feel real."

Reggie is a happily married, middle-aged schoolteacher. He and his wife have sex three or four times a month, enjoy it, enjoy more the feeling of closeness and warmth that's part of

43

the act. Then Reggie's mother, for whom he had a considerable amount of affection, dies. Soon afterward his sexual pattern undergoes a remarkable change. Suddenly he's hungry for sex, wants to make love almost nightly to his wife. At first she's astonished, bemused—then she grasps the message behind the intensity of his need. "Help me, comfort me, support me," is what he's saying with his new-found ardor.

Leo is a well-off investment broker, his stunning wife Vivian a discontented homemaker who now regrets having given up a promising music career to marry. Leo travels, meets important people, develops in stature. Vivian feels powerless and lacks any sense of achievement. They talk about her resentments but Leo can't really grasp them. Their sex life reflects their basic struggle. Leo wants more sex, Vivian wants less. What Leo's desire communicates is, "If I make you sexually happy you won't be so dissatisfied or bitch so much about your lot in life." Vivian readily picks up this signal; for her sex now means, "If I let him satisfy me I put myself even more in a position of enslavement."

What Doreen, Mark, Reggie, Leo, and Vivian illustrate is that there's more to sex than erotic pleasure. For that matter, there's more to sex than saying, "I love you," or, "I want you." The meaning that sex has for us is a communication all its own, a message we send out via myriad little cues to the people with whom we engage in it. Of course, not every sexual experience is rife with hidden meanings, or meanings of great import, yet we do bring to the sex act not only our phalluses and our vaginas, not only the wish to feel good, but a whole constellation of other wishes, fears, and needs.

The remarkable thing about sex is that it can say anything we want it to say. And what we have to say can be constant or can change—change with our moods of the moment, with different sexual partners, or with changed feelings about our partners. It may be helpful, in terms of self-awareness, to glance down the list that follows. It's a list of the more common motivations for having sex and the messages they spark. See if any strike a familiar chord, if you recognize any as a pattern with which you have more than passing acquaintance:

People have sex to:

—bestow pleasure ("Feel good, feel good, feel good")

—demonstrate love ("You and I are one now")

—be dutiful ("Don't say I never gave you anything")

—have excitement ("We'll stir things up")

—prove themselves ("Bet you never met anyone like me before")

—show off ("Look! No hands!")

—relax ("Nothing like it for the nerves")

—get acquainted ("The better to know you")

—control ("Well, who's knuckling under now?")

—suffer ("I'll be sorry later")

—punish ("You'll be sorry later")

—feel close ("It's so warm and snuggly")

—satisfy curiosity ("Always wondered what you'd be like")

—gain revenge ("If only my spouse could see me now!")

—commit themselves ("You have my all")

—settle an argument ("What a way to make up")

—taunt ("You think this is all I'm capable of?")

—be rebellious ("Fucking you is fucking the world")

—get reassurance ("Make everything okay again")

—cuddle ("Let's do it quick, then hold me tight")

—squelch loneliness ("Prove to me I'm not alone")

—offer cheer ("I'll make you forget everything")

—be liked ("*Now* don't you think I'm nice?")

—be degraded ("See how rotten I am?")

—degrade ("See how rotten you are?")

—have a diversion ("They're showing reruns tonight, anyway")

_____

_____

You fill in the blanks. The list is only partial, after all, and if you reflect upon it you may come up with a revealing reason of your own. The object, though, isn't to tear yourself apart emotionally but to understand yourself better in relation to sex and the sexual signals you convey.

SEX AS A WEAPON

As a few items on that list above suggest, sex makes a great weapon if one has the psychic stomach for it. When so used, the sexual arena becomes a battlefield, each message a bullet that unerringly finds its emotional mark. Cleverly employed, sex can shatter a partner's ego, tear down his self-esteem, make him a slave of sorts. It's communication, to be sure—but of the most destructive sort.

Sex can be used as a weapon in any kind of relationship, one that lasts for years or one that has a two-hour lifespan. I know a divorcee who pretends happiness but, after two husbands, is a very angry woman and shows it. When she meets a new male she's immediately flirtatious and has him work up heady fantasies. Invariably, she and the man end up at her apartment for a nightcap. But then ugly reality sets in; the poor man who has been so teased and tantalized is suddenly, calculatedly, thrown out. Her teasing is a revenge on all men—and most of the ones she meets don't return to get shot down a second time.

Sex is often used as a weapon in unhappy marriages or in those with lopsided power balances where one partner is very dominant, the other very passive. As a Family Service Association of America study on the treatment of marital problems puts it, "sex is a primary battleground of marital friction."

That stands to reason: given its explosively emotional nature, and the fact that anyone can play, sex is a natural for that kind of thing. But even in relationships that seem to work relatively well sex is sometimes used underhandedly.

Here are the more popular ways it happens:

"If you don't, I won't." More of a favorite with women, though not exclusively used by them. It's the manipulative use of sex in order to gain something, and there are echoes in it of prostitution.

The idea is to provoke the partner into wanting sex, and then denying him sex, until he gives in to something. Some people use the technique to get a new car or fur coat, others to wangle a vacation in Europe for the family or private school for the kids.

It isn't always as crass and cold as it sounds; some wives who are practiced in the technique perform in such a sweet, low-key way it hardly seems reminiscent of prostitution.

"Hands off, you haven't been good." The idea is to withhold sex as a way of punishing one's partner for bad behavior. People who do this feel themselves morally justified, as if they're using sex on the side of good against evil. Sometimes it's the only means they know to keep an errant or irresponsible spouse in line. But it's a self-defeating game: one withholds sex, the other withholds something else to punish the first for withholding sex, the struggle remains constant or escalates.

"Not interested—guess why." Another form of withholding sex. According to Robert Sunley of the Family Service Association of Nassau County, it's a favorite with white-collar men who are angry with their wives or fed up with their marriages. The men (and women) who play this game won't say what's wrong. They simply hold back on sex and keep their spouses guessing as to the reasons why. A great way to keep one's partner off balance and feeling vaguely guilty without knowing exactly what there is to feel guilty about.

"Tonight and every night." Sunley says that this one appeals more to some blue-collar men. The people who play this one literally do want sex every night as a way of proving their sexuality and showing their mates who's boss. If they don't get sex like clockwork they make life hellish for their recalcitrant spouses.

"You're a lousy lay." A weapon of choice with hostile

mates whose relationship is marked by constant power struggles. Anyone can play, anyone who can think up genital-slashing
lines, because that's what the game consists of—remarks that
hurt, insult, belittle the other in terms of his or her sexuality.
There are nonverbal variations, too, for people who are tongue-
tied or tired of talking. A common one: Supposedly at peace
with each other, the two partners go to a party together. There
one immediately abandons the other and flirts outrageously
with everyone in sight, a way of saying, "Everybody turns me
on but you."

"Now?" The ploy is timing, and it can be used with great
imagination by people who have the imagination. The partner
who masters this method generally doesn't want to have sex but
pretends to want it; the object of the game is to lower the
other's self-esteem. The trick lies in choosing the most inappropriate moment for sex. A husband comes home jittery, preoccupied with a terrible business crisis; sex is the last thing on
his mind—but this is exactly the moment his wife suddenly feels
ardent. A wife is exhausted after a day spent caring for two
sick, whiny kids; that's just when her husband is suddenly eager
for her body.

There's a circular variation of sorts: The first night of the
game one wants sex, the other refuses. The second night the
other wants sex, the first one refuses. The third night—well, you
get the idea, which is, "You didn't do it when I wanted to, so
I'm not going to when you want to."

"I'll take my marbles elsewhere." It's a marital scenario that
has everything and goes like this:

Husband: Let's have sex.

Wife: Nothing doing.

Husband: Okay, if you won't give it to me I'll go play
elsewhere.

Wife: I'm not going to have sex with somebody who sleeps
with other women.

Both win: husband gets tacit permission to have extramarital sex; wife doesn't have to have sex with him, which is what she wanted in the first place. It's the manipulative aspects that put it in the category of sex as a weapon; if they'd faced each other frankly and come to the same arrangement it wouldn't have the corrosive overtones it does.

Note these salient facts about the use of sexual weaponry:

1. Everybody uses sex manipulatively upon occasion; it's destructive only when it becomes a way of life.

2. It's destructive because it's so hostile a form of communication, provoking huge amounts of anger (hidden or otherwise). Nobody really likes to be manipulated; for that matter, underneath it all, nobody really likes to be allowed to get away with manipulating.

3. Sex-as-a-weapon can and does lead to impotence and frigidity, which themselves can be subtle forms of fighting with sex. As one thoughtful therapist pointed out to me long ago, "Every time you see one of these impotence cases clinically, you find that although the man expresses great distress about his misfortune, he also finds a little pleasure in it. He has a way of hooking his wife."

4. There's no clear-cut "victimizer" and "victim" when sex-as-a-weapon becomes an established pattern in a relationship. Even if one of the partners seems like a victim, that partner plays the game by acquiescing in it, maybe even inviting it.

5. If it is a long-existent pattern it's extremely difficult for the persons involved to break out by themselves; professional intervention is usually called for.

INFIDELITY AS SEX TALK

Everything that can be said about sex-as-sex-talk in general can be applied to infidelity—plus a little more. People have extramarital sex to bring some excitement into the routine of their lives, to feel sexy again, to suffer pangs of guilt or cruelty at the hands of an abusive lover, to have a few hours' diversion, to thumb their noses at society. They have extramarital sex because they feel attracted to somebody and want to satisfy their curiosity, because they've fallen in love, because they want to get emotionally close to somebody, because they're intent on creating emotional distance.

The people who commit infidelities in order to distance themselves are basically afraid of getting emotionally close to anyone. Once they find marriage overpowering they run into the arms of lovers or mistresses. Once the extramarital relationship threatens to become too intimate they run back home, in a sense, becoming warmer toward their mates again. So they veer back and forth, to and from an intimacy that both compels and horrifies them. When both spouses share this characteristic they sometimes openly agree to lead lives apart as well as lives together, a consensual arrangement that puts a different cast on the infidelity. It's a way of finding just the right amount of intimacy they can live with, and it can result in a very workable arrangement.

On the other hand, there are people who want to give love and can absorb it the way a blotter absorbs ink, but are married to cold fish. Maybe they needed a cold fish at one point in their lives, but no longer; at any rate, the affair then becomes a means of getting the emotional nourishment that's consistently missing at home. There are long-standing affairs, after all, in which physical love is of minor consequence after a while; emotion is the wheel upon which the relationship turns.

Extramarital sex can serve as a very potent sexual weapon, a way of screwing one's mate while screwing someone else. If you're having sex outside of marriage you can't always tell whether you're doing this; other aspects of the situation may muddy things up. But if you harbor strong resentments against your mate you can be sure that revenge is part of the total picture. The man whose wife refuses to fellate him and who then has a prostitute perform the service certainly wants the enjoyment being fellated gives him; he also gets a kick out of what he's doing behind his wife's back. The wife whose husband neglects her physically and emotionally may find a wonderful sense of completeness with a lover who does give her these things, but she also derives a sense of satisfaction in cheating on the husband who has cheated her. (And probably shows it by dropping little clues to her affair, a form of communication all its own; see Chapter 12.)

Sometimes the spouse who's being cheated actually stage-manages the marital drama to bring on that act of infidelity. It's a devious kind of sex talk and it occurs in numerous ways. Mary hates sex and pushes Joe out of the house, to sleep with other women; she may complain about his unfaithfulness but she also breathes a sigh of relief; she's off the sexual hook. Don accuses Betty of being unfaithful; she isn't, but when he keeps it up long enough she capitulates and takes herself a lover. At this point Don can say, "See, I told you you were no damn good," something he was out to prove from the start. Sally wants to make it with George, a next-door neighbor, so she adroitly maneuvers her husband into bed with George's wife, then falls into George's arms and says, "Somehow I don't feel guilty after what those two have done."

Infidelity is a very complicated form of sex talk because so many characters are involved and because, often, there's so much more going on in the head and heart than with the genitals.

5

The Orgasm and Other Sexual Communications

TAKING A POSITION

If the motivation for sex can be "sex talk" of sorts, what happens during the sex act itself can constitute an even more intimate and potent form of sexual communication. On the grossest level this means the typical sexual boor—the guy who rolls on, rolls off, and goes to sleep—is saying, "Look, it's only my satisfaction I know or care about." It means the woman who lies limply until the man has reached his climax is just as eloquently saying, "You do nothing for me," or, "I'm just doing my duty and you better know it."

Coital positions, too, may be seen as message bearers. The bas-reliefs on Indian temple walls prove mankind's ingenuity for figuring out variations in sexual positioning; their lush abundance also suggests there doesn't have to be a deep, dark significance to any particular position—except the significance of getting as much delight as possible out of sex.

But under certain circumstances sexual positions do have something more to say. And what those positions say are also echoed by nonsexual aspects of behavior on the part of the people involved. Take a classic example: the man who, with almost religious fervor, favors the "missionary" position—that is, the man who insists a woman's place is always on the bottom. This overriding need to have himself on top suggests an overriding need on his part to be dominant, to be in charge.

It's a safe bet this man is bossy in other ways, too—constantly telling his wife or girl friend what to do, checking up on what she does, controlling her spending, and the like. Dr. Sander M. Latts of the University of Minnesota, who also does sex counseling, encountered one husband who aptly described his need to be in the man-on-top position. This man said, "When I'm on top I have better control of the situation." That described him perfectly because he always had to be in control of whatever situation he was in, Dr. Latts recalls, adding, "He'd find it almost intolerable to have it any other way."

Some men who insist on the missionary position don't know any other and would be very unsure of themselves if they tried. But if they show that much reluctance to experiment it amounts to the same thing—they have to be in full control of their environment.

And what about the woman whose need dovetails with that man's—the woman who always has to lie flat on the bed, face up, when she makes love? She, too, may be saying she's afraid to try any other position. She may be saying sex isn't nice and she can bring herself to engage in it only in the most conventional, unexceptional way. There are other possibilities: being on the bottom may also give her the feeling that she's being forced to have it, which in a way removes the responsibility from her. All such feelings can dovetail into one major assumption: woman is to be dominated by man. More than likely, she shows her submissive nature in other respects as well—always deferring to a man, maybe, or acting more the servant than the equal.

So much for the first major position. The second: woman on top. There are pretty good physiological reasons why women—and some men—like it. This position gives women greater freedom to wiggle and thrust; enables them to have more control over the pressure of the penis against the clitoris; moreover, it helps retard men's orgasms because they have less of a chance to move and thrust.

But if a woman is compulsive about being astride a man, if she doesn't really like sex any other way, she's just like the man who has to be on top. She strives to be dominant, always in control; she has to reject anything that even hints at passivity. Such a woman is probably bossy and controlling generally. (One radical member of the women's liberation movement has publicly called upon all sisters always to mount their men, a clear insistence upon female supremacy in bed.)

Then there's the third major sexual position that can carry messages when it's assumed obsessively: the rear-entry one. One therapist I met insisted that every man who enjoys entering a woman from behind at any time has latent homosexual leanings, presumably because it's symbolic of one way homosexual men make love. But every other professional I met correctly scoffed at this rigid interpretation; a sometime desire for any position doesn't make for anything but a sometime desire for that position. When it's a man's overwhelming preference it can suggest homosexual interest. It can also have a different meaning, an interpersonal one. Because it's the one major position in which one partner doesn't face the other it can be a way of saying, "I don't want to look at you," or, "I don't want to take note of your feelings."

Dr. Martin Goldberg of the University of Pennsylvania related a case of this kind in *Medical Aspects of Human Sexuality*. For the husband involved sex wasn't sex unless he could enter his wife from the rear. The marital relationship suggested why. This man was so hostile to his wife in general that "any sexual position that involved facing and kissing her was abhorrent to him." The rear-entry position gave him the chance to have sex without having to be loving or tender.

Symbolically and practically, the side-by-side position is the most egalitarian; thus it may be that if there are any people who insist on side-by-side sex they're rigidly egalitarian. But then, in other of life's transactions they must also measure and count to see that they never cheat or are cheated of a grain that's theirs.

Most people, of course, aren't obsessive about a single position; most fool around, experiment, try a raft of them to see which they like best and feel most comfortable with; they vary positions as the spirit moves them. There's a message implicit in what they do, too—a message having to do with good sense and health and spontaneity.

TELLING IT WITH TECHNIQUES

Sexual techniques, too, may constitute a form of communication. As with positions, this is especially true if there's an overriding urge to employ a particular one.

Almost any technique can serve as an example, so let's take a fairly common one: men who are only turned on sexually, or turned on most intensely, when they're being fellated. Henry is one such. He's mad at, not about, women. He views his penis as an instrument of degradation and when it's in the girl's mouth in effect he's saying, "I'm defiling you." (All the more so if she allows him to ejaculate in her mouth, or if he does so before she can stop him.)

Charles likes girls but fears them and is inordinately anxious about his sexual performance; fellatio is his way of saying, "This way I don't have to put myself to the test of sexual intercourse."

Bob wants the girls to kowtow to him, and the spectacle of a girl kneeling and performing fellatio on him fits right in with that need; this is how he says, "Look at what a big man I am, I can make the girls do this."

Conversely, a woman with an overriding need to perform

fellatio may want to be defiled, or to avoid the test of intercourse, or to gain the feeling that she's sucking away the man's
strength.

By the same token any technique that's consistently *rejected* for reasons other than physical discomfort can be sex
talk of sorts. Sometimes the message simply is, "I'm too inhibited to relax about this," often verbalized as, "It isn't normal." Sometimes it goes deeper. Take men who can't bear to
perform cunnilingus on their female partners. (Not infrequently
they're the same men who must have fellatio.) One possible
message is, "It would put me in a position of subservience,
something I can't abide." Another message might be, "I'm
basically nauseated by the female sex," sometimes voiced as,
"There are a lot of germs formed in the vagina." A third might
be, "I don't want to give you all that pleasure."

The abundance of possible meanings suggests it's no snap
task to unearth the message beneath the act. As with positions,
the compulsion to engage in or reject any single technique has
specific meaning only in the context of the individual's life
experiences and personality, not as an isolated piece of behavior.

Two questions always apply:

1. What significance does the particular technique have for
the person involved?

2. And how does this fit into his overall pattern of relating
and communicating?

Positions, too, can be assessed the same way. But, clearly,
it's no parlor game.

THE ORGASM AS LINGO

We're accustomed to thinking about the orgasm as a delight, a release, a promised thrill, or something that life has
cheated us on. We're not accustomed to thinking about the

orgasm as language. Yet it can be a valid and important medium of expression. It can say, "I love you," "I hate you," and a host of subtler things. Love may be communicated, for instance, by an explosive, uninhibited release whose power—perhaps reflected by look, touch, or word—conveys, "Nobody else could make me feel the way you do." Hate may be conveyed very simply— by not having an orgasm at all. Some women, those engaged in power struggles with their partners, gain a special pleasure from withholding: "He wants to screw; okay, I'll give him a royal screwing and cut him down to size." (Withholding can convey many other messages, of course, an important one being, "I don't dare give myself this pleasure.")

Orgasm rather neatly lends itself to a competitive fight between husband and wife. They can always fight over whose orgasm counts for the most and who has the greater burden of satisfying the other. All kinds of bitter messages can zip back and forth like so many verbal bullets, which in a neurotic way may provide more satisfaction than orgasm itself.

There are sexually insecure people who wait for orgasms— their own or their sex partners'—with fear and trembling; each orgasm is like a missive from the gods, affirming or negating their sexual prowess. Such people act as living gauges; they count and measure orgasms—how many? how powerful?—and if the orgasms arrive in sufficient strength and number it tells them once again what they so desperately need to know: "I'm truly masculine," or, "I'm truly feminine."

There are also sexual clock watchers (usually men) who get their reassurance by observing how long they can keep going before they reach orgasm. One such man literally put a clock by his bed and timed himself. If he couldn't last for at least three quarters of an hour, he concluded, "I'm slipping." Another man was fond of saying, "I screw a woman until she screams for mercy." Such men are really saying, "Sex is a battlefield and I'm going to take my gun and mow them down." Often they undergo a metamorphosis in the eyes of women they're with:

first they're seen as wonderful lovers; eventually, as cruel and sadistic persons.

Mental-health professionals know that intensity of orgasm in both women and men can vary considerably, not only with different partners but also with the same person at different times. (The masturbatory orgasm isn't always the same, either.) It can be a cataclysmic experience—"oceanic," some people like to call it. It can be a very pleasant tingle. It can be a weak, dribbling kind of response.

What makes the difference? Physical factors as well as emotional ones. A person's energy level, general state of health, placement in terms of biochemical rhythm—all count. So does frequency of sex activity. Sexual gluttons, like gustatory ones, usually find the meal becoming an increasingly less voluptuous experience. When weak little orgasms follow frenzied sexual activity it's the body's way of signaling, "Lay off awhile," which could be translated to mean, "Aren't you overdoing things a bit?"

Dr. Arnold A. Lazarus of Yale talks about "optimal deprivation," the point at which peak desire and orgasmic intensity can be expected. This varies from person to person, he says, usually ranging from eight to forty-eight hours after last intercourse.

Some of the emotional factors that have a lot to do with orgasmic intensity are: a person's mood (the more of a buildup of anticipation the more intense the orgasm is apt to be), how he feels about himself and his partner, the sex act itself.

Attitudinal factors are very important. Dr. Judd Marmor, who directs the Divisions of Psychiatry at Los Angeles' Cedars-Sinai Medical Center, points to anxiety, guilt, and depression as being especially powerful hindrances in achieving orgasms in interpersonal relationships.

"One aspect in having a good orgasm is the ability to enter into an erotic experience without any inhibiting anxieties," he says. "A very common source of anxiety is concern about one's sexual performance. Others are fear that one isn't attractive to one's partner, or not as good a lover as the next person."

Thus, a weak orgasm can, quite simply, express, "I'm scared."

Anger is an emotion that can work either way—cut down on orgasmic intensity or, when suppressed rage or outrage is allowed to explode fully in a sexual encounter, result in an orgasm of high intensity. There are, after all, people who can experience satisfactory orgasms only when they've whipped themselves into a rage. (Some use real whips.) To say the least, they don't present a picture of glowing mental and sexual health. And it's not in the sexual encounter but in the venting of rage that they receive their ultimate joy.

LOVE, LUST, AND ORGASM

Many mental-health professionals give sexual counsel somewhat in accordance with the following equations:

Love + Tenderness = Intense Orgasm

Natural Feelings + Lack of Tenderness = Less Intense Orgasm

This follows the romantic precept that only in an atmosphere of love does sex become ultimately rewarding. All things being equal, it's certainly much more enjoyable and gratifying to have sex with somebody one cares deeply about than with somebody one doesn't. But love and sex are more complicated than that. Love messages and sex messages are not, after all, synonymous—yet when they're seen as being so the result can be sexually inhibiting.

According to Dr. Lazarus, what specifically happens in such cases is this: during the sexual encounter one partner concentrates so much on the love or affection he feels for the other partner that his sex impulses are diffused, the result being a markedly lessened erotic atmosphere.

An example is provided by some nonorgasmic but loving wives who say they don't mind not reaching orgasm because they feel warm and close when making love with their husbands. "I find they're so much into the affectional plane that their energies are dissipated," says Dr. Lazarus. "Their energies are deflected from their own genitals."

Despite the popular assumption that women especially are at their sexual best only in a love relationship, it isn't necessarily so. At a Yale debate on love and sex, Dr. Lazarus reports, many women noted a difference in their response with men they were and weren't emotionally involved with. Looking back on it they found that their best orgasms were had with men they were *less* involved with. As for sex with men with whom they had an affectional relationship, they described it as a much more satisfying experience overall—but a less erotic one.

What goes on here? What goes on, possibly, is that either the women or their lovers or both see love as gentle, tender, sex as aggressive, assaulting; and aren't able to reconcile the two. So what's sent out during sex are tender signals—but signals lacking enough erotic content.

Consider Allan, a law student in love with a beautiful classmate named Marie. In their lovemaking Allan was always soft and gentle; not wanting to hurt Marie, he always held himself in check.

Back in his hometown one Christmas vacation he met Rose, a pretty—and pretty bitchy—hometown girl who teased and taunted and angered him, finally provoking him to have sex with her. Allan's anger made him thrust hard and vigorously while they had sex. At the end he expected her to call him a monster. Instead, she said, "Wow, are you terrific!"

Allan was stunned—but no dummy. At school again after the holidays he forced himself to make love to Marie in the way he had with that girl in his hometown. He half expected the worst, but Marie's reaction was, "Why haven't you always made love to me like that!"

People who can't reconcile love with the vigorous, powerful, thrusting, abandoned component of good sexuality are most likely unconsciously associating sex with shame and guilt. They operate on a variant of the old sexual double standard. There's no philosophical difference, after all, between, "You don't do it with somebody you love," and, "You only do it a certain careful way with somebody you love."

In effect, Allan had been saying, "I can't believe a nice woman—a woman I love and respect—could really like it if we let ourselves completely go." Some women who have trouble letting themselves go physically and orgasmically with the men they love function somewhat the same way: they're transported by loving images, not genital images, because they don't find genital images consistent with love. They hold back and—often—also signal their partners to hold back.

On the other hand, people who can love and lust without seeing a contradiction between the two—those people don't block their eroticism. They find, as did the rare self-actualizing people studied by the late Dr. Abraham H. Maslow, that orgasm with a love partner is the most intense and ecstatic they've ever experienced. Their happy messages to each other are, "I love you and trust you and merge with you and let myself completely go with you."

And that's exactly what they do.

6

Into Yourself: Sexual Fantasies

UNIVERSALITY AND GUILT

There are people who say they've never fantasized about sex, but it's hard to take them seriously. The act of fantasizing is a universal one and the act of fantasizing about sex is just as universal, the most private of sexual languages. Sexological studies show that the degree to which people have—and are aroused by—sexual fantasies varies considerably. Age, social class, schooling, and other factors play a part. But to imagine a person who has never once gamboled in a garden of erotica of his own conjuring, not as a child, not during adolescence, never afterward—that's in itself fantastic.

People have fantasies and daydreams (which are elaborated fantasies) about sex, but some can't admit it even to themselves. Marriage counselors and social workers tell me that of all the intimate stuff that's sometimes difficult to pry out of clients, sexual fantasies are the most difficult. Some clients talk readily about everything—except their sexual fantasies.

The impression I gain, in talking to both professionals and nonprofessionals, is that sexual fantasies are not only universal, they're universally guilt-producing. Why? Maybe because here all inhibitions can be cast aside; there need be no outer limits to the blue movies we produce inside our heads. Maybe because somewhere within us there lurks a fear that others can see inside our heads and divine what we're imagining. Maybe because there's a lingering remembrance of childhood-adolescent fantasies in which a parental figure had a starring role. For whatever reason, and to whatever degree, sex fantasies commonly produce guilt.

Yet here's an intriguing phenomenon from which we can derive something practical: people who have the most trouble coping with their sexual fantasies—who feel the most guilty about them—are those who act as though their fantasies were real. In other words, they fail to distinguish between fancy and fact; for them, thinking about it is the same as doing it. So they chastise themselves. They think they're terrible.

The healthy approach to sexual fantasies, counsels Dr. Warren L. Jones, a psychoanalyst, is to recognize them for what they are—figments of the imagination.

"If you can accept your fantasy life you become decreasingly apprehensive and insecure and guilt-ridden about it," he says. "The very fact that you're able to identify the fantasy for what it is, a fantasy, does it."

WHAT, WITH WHOM, AND WHY

All fantasies reflect unmet needs, wishes, or desires—whether fleeting or long-standing. A woman sees an attractive man at a party and for a few idle moments wonders how it would be to have sex with him; fleetingly her musings turn into a fantasy as she sees herself and him locked in an erotic embrace. A husband is turned on by big breasts; when he makes love to his small-breasted wife he sees large, large breasts in his mind's eye. A girl having an affair with a man imagines him with her when she's alone and masturbating; one young woman told me she systematically changes her fantasy lovers to correspond to her real ones when she masturbates, and there have been numerous such changes. Some husbands and wives fantasize doing sexy things their partners won't do with them; fantasies of this kind may accompany either masturbation or intercourse. I encountered a salesman who prides himself on a peculiar kind of monogamy: when he sleeps with another woman on one of his sales trips, he assured me, he always imagines it's his wife there in bed with him.

When it comes to sexual fantasies, the variations are endless.

A sexual fantasy doesn't have to lead to arousal, of course, but there's no question that sexual fantasies are the cheapest, safest, and handiest aphrodisiacs available. One of the Kinsey studies on the sexual behavior of Americans shows that a much more substantial number of men than women fantasize while masturbating. Some women may question this finding, but there's no questioning the fact that there are a handful of women in the world who can do something no man seems able to—fantasize themselves to orgasm. Several young women told me they use sexual fantasies to help them reach orgasm during intercourse. One literally fantasizes reaching orgasm—and that's how she reaches it. Another conjures up a heavy petting session as her aid to coital orgasm; the reason is that she, a late starter, has learned to climax while petting but can't do it yet during coitus. At times the fantasy works.

Traditionally the sex fantasies of women and men have had a different quality to them, and to a considerable extent probably still do. Women's fantasies are apt to be more romantic and tender, sex is more often seen in the context of love, there's more of a suggestion of continuity—a wild sex scene, for instance, concludes with the couple living happily ever after. Men's fantasies are apt to be more immediate, more explosive; men are much more likely to see themselves as sexual superbeings, conquerors whose weapon is the erect penis.

But these stereotypical patterns are changing—especially for women, as the expectations of women in American society change. A number of New York career women talked to me about their sexual fantasies and in not one instance did the fantasy fit the general pattern. Alice, for instance, has a recurrent fantasy of being with a desirable man at a party; suddenly the two are so overcome with desire they have sex right then and there, in front of everybody. Betty talked of being one of ten girls locked in a room with a man who hasn't shown much interest in her; the man is forced to have sex with them all, starting with her. Sylvia's fantasies are sometimes triggered by the sight of teenage boys with their "slender bodies and their eagerness," as she put it; she imagines seducing them, teaching them all about sex, being the woman of the world with them. Sylvia, I should add, is just twenty-three, and not very experienced sexually.

The most striking thing about most of the fantasies I heard from either sex was their ordinariness. To be sure, there are men who can't have sex unless they dress up like Napoleon or prance around on all fours like horses; their fantasies reflect their bizarre tastes. There's also the sizable sadomasochistic sexual subculture, whose fantasies of whips and chains and other forms of torture or degradation can sometimes be wildly imaginative (at least upon first hearing).

Yet most people aren't really in such special categories; most people's fantasies tend to be rather banal and repetitious. It's as hard to imagine creatively different, entertaining sex scenes for personal consumption as it is to write them for public titillation.

FANTASY LOVERS

Question: Here you are, solidly entrenched in a relationship, marital or otherwise, yet now and then, when you make love to your partner, some other person's face and body appears.

What's happening? Answer: What's happening is that you're in company with millions of other men and women who now and again cull up a fantasy lover while making love to their own partner.

That fantasy lover can be a famous movie star like Paul Newman or Sophia Loren, a former boy friend or girl friend, the guy or gal next door, an attractive person you passed on the street earlier in the day. Whoever the fantasy figure is, you may wonder if there's something wrong with the practice—if it shows a serious, deep-seated dissatisfaction with your real-life sex partner; if it's a form of infidelity you're practicing; if you're reducing your real partner to little more than an object; and so on.

To be very technical, the need to fantasize a substitute for the real-life partner does show some dissatisfaction (though it needn't be strong), and the practice is, in the strictest sense of the term, an act of infidelity. But it's difficult to imagine any two people whose relationship is totally devoid of dissatisfaction, and it's equally difficult to imagine even the most monogamous of relationships completely devoid of an occasional psychic infidelity. Just looking at another person for a moment with mild interest can constitute that.

Therefore, it isn't useful to approach life on terms of such utter strictness. Dr. Ruth Aaron, who is on the staff of the Southern California Psychoanalytic Institute, offers some sensible advice: If your relationship with your real-life partner is essentially a good one, that fantasy of yours will have a paradoxical effect. For a little while you'll have isolated yourself from your partner in the deeper recesses of your mind. But when you've both had your orgasms, and you're feeling warm and close and gratified, it's your own spouse or lover again, not some fantasy figure, to whom you snuggle up and with whom you fall asleep.

Things aren't always that idyllic, of course. But even if two people have relationship problems which they're unwilling or unable to tackle, and fantasies help them remain sexually active with each other, there's no reason not to use them.

For all of that, one word of caution. It's possible to be so caught up with the fantasy figure that you lose sight of the real-life partner altogether; when the partner feels this, it can cause unhappiness. "When we make love I always have the feeling my husband's not with me," one wife complained. "I have the feeling he's not in the room, he seems to be going his own way." She was hurt at being excluded but she had never mentioned her feelings to him. She should have; then he could have tried to find ways of keeping his fantasies without excluding her—or pondered on the deeper problem of why he needed to detach himself so consistently and thoroughly from her.

NORMAL AND ABNORMAL

So-called deviate or abnormal fantasies puzzle, startle, disturb, and alarm people most. When the fantasy content is explicitly voyeuristic, exhibitionistic, sadistic, masochistic, or homosexual, the immediate inward reaction often is, "My God, what does this say about me?"

One thing it says about you is that you're perfectly human. It's a rare person who has never had, even fleetingly, voyeuristic, exhibitionistic, sadistic, masochistic, or homosexual fantasies. Moreover, unless you're really obsessed with a particular fantasy, you don't have to worry about either being or doing what the fantasy suggests. It's no more plausible to assume you'll be running naked down Main Street one day (if that's the content of your fantasy) than to assume you're actually going to commit murder because you're so angry with somebody you wish him dead.

The very concept of "normal" and "abnormal" fantasies is an oversimplification. A young man, say, can have the most normal (conventional) fantasy in the world—having conventional sex with a girl—but if he's hung up on the fantasy and thinks of little else, or if the fantasy serves as a substitute for reality, for actually attempting heterosexual relations, it's abnormal. On the other hand, a man may fantasize another man while making love to his wife and have it be a normal experience in the sense that it helps him to perform better and doesn't interfere with his general functioning.

In any event, it's a bad idea to categorize or attempt to analyze your own fantasies, to make something concrete of them in terms of your personality and your sex life. It's a self-destructive, self-defeating exercise because you're not trained to do it, you're too emotionally involved, and you're most likely to be way off the mark and worry yourself needlessly.

Rape fantasies are a case in point. They're common in adolescent girls, and some mature women have them, too. The woman who fantasizes rape may actually want to be sexually brutalized. Much more likely, the fantasy springs from her ambivalent feelings about sexual intercourse; she both wants sex and feels very guilty about having it. To be raped is to be forced to have sex; to be forced to have it is to have it without personal responsibility; to have it without taking responsibility is to be off the hook in terms of guilt feelings.

Homosexual fantasies are another example. They can be very disturbing, especially to men who have always prided themselves on how masculine they are. A repetitive homosexual fantasy involving explicit same-sex lovemaking may indicate a strong wish for homosexual experience. On the other hand, one can fantasize hugging, kissing, or fondling a same-sex person (say, a friend) without narrowly homosexual desire; the impulse can have its wellspring primarily in a desire to express affection. We do have affection for same-sex persons as well as opposite-sex persons, after all, and sex in its various forms is one of the ways we show affection.

A sexual fantasy can serve explicitly nonsexual ends: Dr.

Bernard H. Shulman of Northwestern University Medical School has reported the intriguing case of a salesman who couldn't cope with frustration and had homosexual fantasies whenever a problem occurred on the job; as soon as the fantasy came to mind he dropped everything he was doing and spent the rest of the day worrying about the fantasy. It was a way of avoiding dealing with the real-life problem. Once he was made aware of this, the homosexual fantasies stopped occurring.

Rather than attempting to analyze a particular fantasy or trying to gauge its "normality quotient," it's much more useful simply to recognize the importance of sexual fantasies in our lives. Our fantasies can:

—Add spice to our sex experiences.

—Help make up for what we feel is lacking in real life.

—Be an acceptable way of handling wishes or desires we perceive as unacceptable in terms of actual behavior.

—Aid us in working through such unacceptable desires, enabling us to modify them into acceptable behavior. A woman who has rape fantasies, for instance, can encourage her sexual partner to strip her and be forceful when they have sex—thus lending illusion to reality, and reality to illusion.

Just because sexual fantasies can be a positive force in our lives, however, doesn't mean they necessarily have to be. Fantasies can work destructively as well as constructively. Your sexual fantasies are okay unless they:

—Preoccupy you, consuming much of your time and energy.

—Weigh you down with guilt, with immobilizing shame.

—Cause you endless worry and concern about your normality.

—Pull you into a depression.

—Make you feel you'll lose control and act in antisocial ways or ways that are repugnant to you consciously.

—Make you behave in ways that are distressing to your sex partner.

If you react to a particular fantasy in one such way then it's clear that, regardless of its content, the fantasy is bad for you. Under these circumstances the best thing you can do for yourself is to seek competent professional counsel. You may need nothing more than reassurance—but those danger signals indicate you do need something in the way of help.

SHARING FANTASIES

A young professor and his wife, both working in the same Midwestern college, sometimes exchange fantasies. He tells her his fantasies about a pretty girl in his class; she tells him her fantasies about a boy in her class she finds attractive. They go on at length about the sex experiences they'd like to have with these respective students. Then, provoked to a fever pitch of arousal, the professor and his wife make love. They call what they do a "super turn-on."

I know a wife who made the mistake of telling her doctor husband about a homosexual fantasy of hers. Her husband was aghast. He berated her, called her a lesbian, stormed out of the house. Later he calmed down and apologized but their life together hasn't been the same since.

When sex partners share their sex fantasies the result can be fantastic in terms of adding fun, pleasure, and intimacy to the relationship. But the result can also be disastrous, as it was for that doctor's wife.

When people disclose their fantasies to spouses or other sex partners, it's usually for one of two reasons. The first is to get reassurance; to be told, "You're still okay with me, you're normal." The second is to make the fantasy a part of sex play itself, to use it for arousal or for acting out the stuff of the fantasy. Reassurance, however, might best be gotten from another source. You can't be sure how your partner will react. If the reaction is negative it can affect your sexual and even your emotional relationship. Once the fantasy is out, it's out; it can't be erased.

As for using fantasies for aphrodisiac purposes, this can be a one-sided or a mutual arrangement. One husband has it in his head that it would be great sometimes to have sex with a prostitute. So now and then, at his urging, his wife puts on flashy makeup, fits a blond wig over her black head of hair, dresses in a garish costume he got for the occasion, and struts around like a street whore. The wife says she doesn't get a kick out of pretending to be a prostitute, but doesn't mind pleasing her husband this way occasionally—and enjoys his ardor when she does.

Fantasy-sharing works out best when it's mutual and when each partner's fantasies merge with the other's; a man who fantasizes having sex with a prostitute, for instance, can work out a kind of make-believe reality with a sex partner who now and then fantasizes herself as a prostitute. Some couples who share fantasies are aroused simply by the talk; they don't feel they have to translate imagery into action. It's far from unusual, observes Dr. James L. Hawkins of the Indiana University–Purdue University Medical Center, for husbands and wives to stimulate themselves and each other by orgy talk. They go on at length about what they'd do at orgies—but never go near a real one. Dr. Hawkins has also counseled couples who finally decide to try the real thing—and have the experience end up as a disaster, the husband impotent, the wives anxious and nonorgasmic. "Go back to the make-believe," he counsels such couples.

If the idea of sharing sex fantasies appeals to you, but you haven't shared them before, keep in mind that the outcome can be unpleasantly explosive. Observe these cautions:

Think about why you want to share a fantasy, what you hope to get out of the experience, and what you hope your partner will get out of it. Mutual pleasure is the most legitimate aim.

Sound your partner out, stressing that this is an experience that calls for broad-mindedness on both your parts. If the reaction is negative, forget it; this is supposed to be a turn-on, not a turn-off.

Encourage mutual, rather than unilateral, sharing. Start with a mild fantasy, working up gradually to the more far-out ones. At each step of the way gauge what Dr. Hawkins calls your partner's "internal security system." If you sense discomfort, ease off; if you anticipate shock, skip that particular fantasy. Homosexual fantasies are always potentially explosive, and some spouses are also especially uptight if the fantasy concerns a former boy friend or girl friend, or a former spouse.

You'll discover your own best times for sharing; many people who engage in the practice do so as part of the play of foreplay.

How to Talk to a Sex Partner

7

Using the Language of Sex

VERBAL FOREPLAY

The incident that follows was told to me by a trade magazine reporter named Sally, who's twenty-two, bright, pretty, and—for her age, at least—unusually sophisticated in the sexual realm. She was interviewing an aggressive, successful businessman in the commercial arts field over lunch one day, when suddenly he stopped talking about his business dealings and looked at her sharply.

"How old are you?" he demanded.

"Just turned twenty-two."

"Graduated from college?"

"Yes."

"When?"

"Two years ago."

"How come?"

"I skipped grades."

"That's interesting. Do you want to fuck?"

Sally's heart skipped a beat. There'd been no preliminaries; his question had come out of the blue. As if from a distance she heard a small voice, her own, saying, "Yes."

"That's good," the businessman calmly replied—and just as abruptly shifted the conversation back to the interview. Sally forced herself to carry on but she was literally shaking, one part of her mind refusing to believe he had asked what he had asked.

At the very end of the meal, as they were getting ready to leave, he made another abrupt conversational shift: "What time do you want to meet me tonight?"

Flustered, Sally said something about meeting him right after work.

"What do you want to do when you fuck?" he demanded. When she stared at him wordlessly, he added, "How do you fuck? What do you like? I want to know what to get ready for."

Sally mumbled something and fled back to her office. The afternoon was shot for her; she spent most of it doodling hearts, flowers, and penises on a scratch pad.

The first thing he said when she met him at his office after work was, "Well, did you think about me this afternoon? What did you think about?"

She started to say something but by this time both of them were ready to substitute action for words and had sexual relations there on his office couch.

Recalling this experience and others she'd had with the same man, Sally told me, "He would just get you so hot talking about it, thinking about it—just get you really worked up like nobody's business. It was fantastic."

There was nothing shy or reticent about Sally, yet the way that businessman had handled words reduced her to trembling adolescent eagerness. Tone, timing, the abrupt shift into and out of sex talk, the specific words he chose and the artful questions he asked combined to produce an effect as heady as a sexual stimulant.

And that's the point of Sally's experience. Words can be a very effective sexual stimulant because talking sex means thinking sex, and thinking sex means fantasizing sex, and fantasizing sex leads to a stirring of erotic impulses.

In effect words can be not a substitute for foreplay but an integral part of it, as arousing as a caress. Recently a friend of mine took his new girl friend to a rather staid party where I was also present. The two remained huddled on a settee, whispering and giggling to each other, and making it clear they wanted no intruders. It was evident something special was going on, and after about an hour they left rather hurriedly.

Later my friend explained that they'd somehow gotten started on a game of telling each other just what they'd do with each other if they were completely alone. Their game got them more and more aroused, he said—"like, verbally, we were at each other's crotches the whole time"—until finally they had to run out and be alone and do the things they'd talked about.

Verbal foreplay can work anywhere—over lunch, at a party, while petting; there are no rules other than that both parties be receptive to the idea. You can play the game with a new acquaintance, with a spouse, with a bed companion you know well. Some persons have a natural feel for the game, as some persons have a natural feel for the physical aspects of love-making; others can learn it as they learn how to handle sex play in general.

One thing you can't legitimately get from a book are the lines to say. "My hands want to be all over your marvelous breasts right now," can sound stilted and unnatural when said by one man in one situation, deliciously exciting when said by another man in another situation. "I want to unzip your pants and do all sorts of crazy things," sounds crude or banal when breathed by one woman in one circumstance, passionate when breathed by another woman in another circumstance.

The words have to come from you or they sound phony. They have to fit the situation or they can be ridiculous. They have to be matched to the person with whom you want to engage in verbal foreplay or run the risk of sounding very offensive. Few men could probably have carried off the kind of verbal foreplay Sally's businessman engaged in, and a good many women would have been revolted by it.

Say what *you* feel, not what you think sounds offbeat or flattering or dramatic or romantic. Respond to the particular man or woman with whom you want to play verbally—to whatever it is he or she evokes in you. What is it about this person that turns you on? What special little looks, gestures, or quirks especially arouse you? What do you do together that you find delightful? What would you like to do together that you anticipate as being delightful? And on a more general plane, why do you like this person? What is it about this particular individual that makes you want to be together, makes you feel good?

Let such things be the springboard for verbal foreplay. However halting or inarticulate you may think you sound, your words will be special. They're genuine. They're yours. They come from the heart. And that gives them a real power.

If you two can giggle and joke together, so much the better. Laughter is a better relaxant than a tranquilizer and, anyway, sex isn't really one of mankind's most deadly serious occupations. (Unless, poor soul, one's always wanting to prove something with it.) On the contrary, its pleasures are heightened when it's laced with teasing, giggling, laughing.

As with any other foreplay, you have to have some sensitivity toward the person you're playing with. If it's someone familiar, presumably you know what will arouse, amuse, or offend that person; you know something of the other's style and can catch his mood of the moment. If it's a comparative stranger you want to play with, that's more difficult to do, of course. But even at first meeting people throw out all sorts of cues and signs that are as much a tip-off to what they're like as the words they utter. If you leave yourself really open to the other person, you can often gain a pretty accurate impression in a short time of what he or she is like.

SEDUCTIVENESS VS. SENSUALITY

Have you ever wanted to tell someone how attractive you find him or her? Have you ever wanted to say something like that, nothing more, no ulterior motive in mind—and stifled the impulse for fear of being misunderstood? Many of us have. We assume that saying something like that will sound terribly suggestive—and make the other person either feel uncomfortable or expect a sexual follow-through.

So we bottle up such feelings. The more we bottle them up the more inhibited and awkward we become in using the language of sex under any circumstances—when we do hope to have something sexual evolve as well as when we don't.

Responsible for our reticence is a confusion between seductiveness and sensuality. Many people go on the assumption that being seductive is being sensual, and that being sensual is being seductive. Not so. They're different, and recognizing the difference may help you to be freer in expressing yourself.

Being seductive is being out to seduce, entice, beguile. Seductiveness can be fun, playful, the kind of thing that goes on at Christmas parties. It also can be—and often is—done with serious intent, either to get somebody into bed or to prove to oneself that somebody could be gotten into bed. There's always an element of slyness, of control and manipulation, involved. The person who sends out seductive signals expects some kind of outcome, some response from the person on the receiving end of those signals. This creates uncertainty for both parties, the one who expects a response and the one who's expected to produce. It's why seduction scenes are often characterized by an element of tension.

Sensuality is something else again. When you're being sen-

sual you make no demands, create no expectations, don't operate on the basis of art and artifice, aren't being manipulative.
What you communicate exists for its own sake; either by what
you say or how you say it, you make clear that you're putting
on no pressure. You make clear the other person isn't on the
spot, you expect nothing in return for what you say.

Not long ago a male friend of mine and I were dining in a
restaurant when an uncommonly pretty girl walked in and sat
down nearby. Both the other man and I looked at her with
pleasure. She couldn't help noticing. As we left the restaurant
my friend paused by the girl's table and said, "You're beautiful,
I want to thank you for letting me look at you." They smiled at
each other; he and I left; that was that.

Both the girl and the man had been sensual rather than
seductive: she because she really didn't do anything deliberate
or calculating to attract our attention; he because he candidly
told her how she'd stirred him—but without making her feel
imposed upon or pressured to deal with the situation in any
way.

When you're being seductive you're always in danger of
generating anger or resentment because people don't really like
to be imposed upon. (Habitual seducers are themselves very
angry persons.) When you're being sensual, by contrast, you're
simply saying, "this is how *I* feel, period," which makes no
demands and therefore implies spontaneity and freedom. This
makes it a much more powerful and much less risky form of
communication than is seductiveness.

TALKING AND DOING

Couples that enjoy themselves the most sexually are couples
whose approach to sex is very pragmatic. They know (or discover) what they like and don't like sexually; they act on those

likes and dislikes; they're free, open, direct, and spontaneous about their sexual conduct and practices.

All this requires more than an absence of inhibitions or an approach to sex grounded on the commonsense conviction that what they do sexually is nobody's business but their own. It also requires communication. It requires language. Dr. Arnold Lazarus of Yale, who has encouraged students to be more verbally expressive in their sexual relationships, puts it nicely: "I can't feel what you feel, you can't feel what I feel, but we can do what no animals can do—we can tell each other. We can show and describe and keep each other in the picture the whole time."

There are men and women who can be very candid about their sexual preferences even on a first encounter, as candid as they are about the foods and drinks they enjoy. Does she like her breasts firmly grasped, her inner thighs gently stroked? Does he like his ear tongue-flicked, his scrotum caressed? *Before* engaging in sexual intercourse they compare notes, make their pet turn-ons and turn-offs known to each other, operate on the notion that the way fully to enjoy the experience is to get directly to what's the most pleasurable, what's the most fun— rather than to have to come upon these things accidentally, by tedious trial-and-error efforts, or not at all.

There are men and women who take full responsibility for their own sexual pleasure *during* intercourse; their attitude is, "I'll tell you what's going right and what's going wrong and I trust you to let me know what's pleasing to you and what isn't. That way I don't have to try and guess with you, and maybe guess wrong."

There are men and women who, *after* a sexual encounter, discuss it as other people talk about a meal they've had—what was good, what was so-so, what was bad. They engage in a kind of mutual feedback in which they relive the most exquisite moments ("I loved it when your legs seemed to be very wide and I felt so close to you, so deep in you"), savoring them in retrospect.

I'd guess that the number of men and women who can carry on that kind of communication is very small. Most of us aren't able to be that open with each other. We're too constrained to state what our special preferences are, those kinky little sex things that would give us special delight; some of us are constrained to state them not only at first or second meeting but after decades of living together. We're reluctant to say explicitly what's going on with us during the sex act. We're too embarrassed to talk it over afterward; such joyous celebration of sex is something we're not used to.

Yet this kind of free talk *is* going on and can be a model for the rest of us, no matter how tentatively or haltingly we begin. Talking about sex, like sex itself, requires practice to make—well, if not perfect, at least something that adds to our pleasure.

As Dr. Lazarus remarks, "Talking can make the doing that much better."

8

How to Talk to Your Partner About Sex Problems

TONE AND TIMING

Sylvia is troubled about herself and her husband, Fred. The sexual verve that characterized the first few years of their marriage is missing now. And she misses it. She resolves to have a candid talk with Fred and does so one evening after they've had a good meal and are relaxing on pillows by the fireplace. Fred tells Sylvia that he, too, has felt something lacking in their sex life and guesses it's because he has become preoccupied with business matters. They agree to take a short trip by themselves soon, a sexy weekend, leaving their children with relatives.

Clara and Don are similarly troubled; their sex life is also marked by the blahs. But whenever Clara tries to talk to Don about it he balks. She can't get through. Tension rises and they never really get anywhere.

Same problem, opposite results. Why? Because Sylvia's and Clara's approaches were markedly different. Sylvia chose a time when she and her husband were relaxed, warmed by a good meal, at ease with each other. Clara never chose the time; the time chose her. She plunged right in when the problem was uppermost in her mind—that is, when she was especially disappointed and resentful. Inevitably, then, her approach was accusatory rather than conciliatory. She was far readier to serve ultimatums than to explore the problem nonjudgmentally. So Don was always put on the defensive and reacted in kind.

Sex talk, expecially sex talk that centers on a problem, is potentially very explosive for couples. Inevitably, the man's reaction is, "What does this say about my masculinity?" Inevitably, the woman has feelings about herself and her femininity. The temptation is to ward off a real talk, to refuse to engage in the discussion, to argue, to deflect any possible accusation by casting blame first.

Don't start a talk when your anger is riding high; in spite of your best intentions that anger will take over and the talk become an exercise in aggression rather than a search for solutions. Don't talk when either of you is tired, preoccupied, or in a hurry to get somewhere, or has had too much to drink. Pick a relaxed moment, one in which you have plenty of time and there are feelings of affection between you.

Picking the right moment doesn't mean nobody will get hurt. But the hurt feelings will be less intense because what's said is said in a way that's less hurting.

Some people invariably choose the *wrong* time; when that happens what they want, wittingly or unwittingly, is for the talk not to come off. Because deep down they want to dodge the basic issues surrounding the problem, or for whatever other reason, they preordain failure.

Before starting to talk to your partner about a sex problem, ask yourself:

1. Is this the right time?
2. Is this the right place?
3. Am I—are we—really in the right mood to begin?
4. What am I really after?

BREAKING THE ICE

Even in the best of circumstances you may still find it difficult to get that talk going. Maybe the words don't come out the way you want them to; maybe your partner tries to vanish or pleads a headache or attempts to joke out of it—or simply, frankly, refuses to talk.

One of these three techniques may help to break the ice:

1. Use sex manuals. They're handy devices for people who find it easier to read than to talk about sex. Many sex manuals are fairly comprehensive in their treatment of the subject; you shouldn't have trouble finding one that touches on the issue you have in mind. But don't use the book (or pamphlet or magazine article) as a rule book for sexual conduct; use it as a tool for facilitating discussion. It may be easier to say, "Honey, there's something that might be useful for us to read," than, "Honey, there's something I want to talk to you about."

The material can be read separately and then discussed together, or read and discussed together, however suits you best. Once you've begun talking about what the book says it should be easier to slide into your own feelings and concerns.

Some provisos, however: a sex manual can work against you if you choose the wrong one, one that's offensive or otherwise vexing to you or your partner. A more inhibited person, for instance, might well be revolted by one of the very graphic new sex manuals like *The Sensuous Woman* or *The Sensuous Couple.* Also, don't be overly impressed with the specific advice given in any of the books. The advice applies generally; you and your partner are individuals, with your own unique physiological and psychological workings. Sexual advice is helpful only when you can fit it in with your temperament, never when you try to fit yourself (or your partner) into the advice.

Above all, don't use a marriage manual as a club to pound home your point of view. Even if the book factually proves you right and your partner wrong, it doesn't take into account your partner's feelings about the issue at hand. When a book on sex is used as a sexual weapon, useful communication becomes the first victim.

2. *Metacommunicate.* That's a common term in communications theory; it simply means "talk about talking." The technique can be very helpful to get a sex talk off the ground because it gets you into a discussion of why you're having problems discussing the subject. In effect, you're saying, "Look, we can't really seem to get started talking seriously and sensibly about sex. Every time we begin, something happens. So let's not talk about sex. Let's talk about why we're having so much trouble talking about sex."

If the problem is one of acute embarrassment, talk about why you're embarrassed (merely bringing the fact of embarrassment out in the open does a lot to lessen it). If quarrels always erupt, maybe your timing is off or you two fall into other communication traps we'll be exploring. The more you talk about talking sex, the more likely it is you'll eventually shift to the crucial issue you actually want to talk about.

3. *Practice gradualism.* Instead of starting in talking about the big problem, the one that seems to generate so much tension, build up to it gradually. Start in talking about sex in general—be it your reaction to the latest raunchy movie playing at the local cinema, or a sex-related newspaper item, whatever. Slowly, maybe over a period of time, work into your personal problems. The idea is first to get used to talking about sex generally; then it becomes easier to get specific.

Gradualism is especially appropriate if you and your partner aren't really used to sharing deeply felt emotions. To make a sudden plunge into this kind of intimacy isn't likely to work out very well; it's unsettling or confusing to everybody concerned.

"You can't impose feelings by an act of will," the Marriage Council's Dr. Philip Feldman points out. He suggests that the sharing of feelings ought to evolve from the most easily shared ones to the most difficult.

STYLES OF TALK

The Family and Children's Service of Minneapolis offers a very helpful, broad-based communications course named UNITE to engaged and married couples; the course is particularly appropriate to a topic as sensitive as sex. Throughout much emphasis is given to the styles of talk which people use to communicate, the idea being that the style has to fit the occasion or communication breaks down. According to the program, which was developed at the University of Minnesota, there are four styles to choose from:

Conventional. Superficial. Party chit-chat, matter-of-fact comments, anything that leaves out your feelings, is conventional. In the context of sex, a noncommittal remark along the lines of, "It's Wednesday, this is our usual night," would be conventional. It's really not for facing issues or otherwise talking about sensitive matters.

Assertive. When you're being pushy, demanding, dictatorial, manipulative, belittling. Assertive talk is attacking talk. It can lead to arguments—and it's certainly okay to argue at times—but this style isn't recommended for problem-solving.

Speculative. Wishy-washy talk, a way of getting at a problem by gnawing at the edges. You don't really put much of yourself into it. For instance:

"Are you in the mood?"

"Guess so."

Advice, both in terms of giving and receiving, is often speculative:

"Well, I really think you'd feel a lot better if you loosened up more."

"Maybe you're right."

Questions, especially when they become a habitual pattern of communication, are speculative:

"Do you think our sex life is all it should be?"

"Do you?"

"I asked you first."

The speculative style can sometimes ease you into a meaningful talk but it doesn't get much accomplished in its own right because you put so little of yourself into it.

Confronting. This is the style that requires you to confront yourself and your own feelings, and your partner and your partner's feelings. That makes it the most appropriate system when you truly want to reach someone, solve problems, discuss a sensitive issue. When you talk confrontingly you must conform to three specific rules of communication:

1. You speak only for yourself, not for your partner. This means that what you say inevitably has a good deal of "I" in it.

2. You "document"—back up—what you say with examples and illustrations. This again brings you into the picture because you're demonstrating *why* you feel the way you do.

3. You try to *get* some feedback from your partner, on the order of, "Do you read me?" or, "How do you feel about what I've said?"—and you *give* feedback to your partner, on the order of, "Do I read you correctly?" or, "This is how I read you."

In the confronting kind of communication, therefore, you have to be open and revealing, you have to face issues and the emotions they spark.

In essence, each of you says to the other, "I'm not asking you for your feelings until I tell you what mine are. Until I tell you what my worries and concerns and needs are. I'm going to share *myself* with you first and then ask you to tell me where *you* are."

Both of you, then, give each other permission to reveal yourselves and to explore issues on a very basic level of honesty, clarity, and directness.

USING CONFRONTATION

It's evident that confronting talk is risky talk, the riskiest you can engage in. It's risky when both of you engage in it equally; it's riskier still when you're the one who begins using it

or uses it unilaterally. (Well, someone has to start.) Will your
partner be as open as you are? Will your partner somehow use
your openness against you? Will your partner scoff or sneer or
become angry?

There's an ultimate risk—that once you open up the subject
it rebounds on you. This often happens, since sex problems
generally are neither partner's "fault" so much as they are a
combination of circumstances to which both partners contribute.

A case from the Marriage Council's files will illustrate. A
married couple sought help because of the wife's inability to
reach orgasm. Both partners saw it as "her" problem. But as
they began to open up in counseling sessions the husband
admitted something for the first time: he had his own doubts,
doubts about his sexual adequacy, about his ability to stimulate
a woman and make her responsive. Once this came to light he
began to see his wife in a much more sympathetic light than
before. And once he began to assume some of the responsibility
for their sexual problems the two were able to work on them
mutually. In time the wife did become more responsive.

Although this incident took place in a clinical setting, the
point applies generally. You don't know where a talk will lead.
If you're really intent on reaching the other person and solving
problems, you must accept this risk.

What's more, when you engage in a confronting kind of talk
you can't take responsibility for your partner's reaction or for
the eventual outcome of the talk. What will happen will happen.
You can only take responsibility for yourself, for your own
involvement in the communication.

All this presupposes a measure of self-confidence; it's an
essential when you're being confronting. As Ron Brazman, who
co-leads a UNITE group at the Family and Children's Service,
aptly puts it, "You really have to trust yourself, that what
you're feeling and thinking is okay, before you can let anybody
in on it."

But then, why shouldn't you be self-confident? Those are

your thoughts, *your* feelings, that you want to express. You have a perfect right to them. Of course they're okay!

It's very humanness is what gives confronting talk its power; properly used, it can actually break down strong resistance.

Example: You want to have a serious talk but your partner artfully dodges it by being flip. You might say, confrontingly, "This is really important to me, and when you joke about it I feel hurt because it doesn't seem as important to you. I know you're not really hearing me."

A few confronting remarks like that and it becomes very difficult for the jokester to keep on joking.

Example: You want to have a calm sex talk but your partner always reacts by attacking you. You might say, "When you start to attack me I really get upset. I find it harder to talk, I feel blamed, scared of you."

Let's suppose your partner replies, "Well, maybe you feel blamed because you feel guilty."

Then you could retort, "When you say something like that I really feel like pulling back and not talking at all about it. I don't know what to do when you make a remark like that."

Again, it's hard for the other person to keep on attacking you when you avoid retaliating but simply express how those attacks make you feel. Your partner's eventual response may not be a warm embrace, but even a noticeable lessening of aggressiveness can lead to a more constructive exchange.

CONFRONTATION AND CRITICISM

What confronting talk does is to create an atmosphere that allows for "open" rather than "closed" (hostile) dialogue. This is especially useful when the talk is of a sensitive or critical nature. Let's take a representative situation of this kind and work with it.

Vicky, let's say, wants Bill to be more aggressive in his

lovemaking. There are a number of ways she could approach this problem.

"Sure would be nice, Bill, if you'd work up a little enthusiasm when we have sex."

Poor, poor approach. She's being snide, bitchy, really out to wound Bill. Most likely his reaction with be either to withdraw or to try to wound her in turn. What he's least likely to do is to address himself to her central concern.

"Bill, why don't you loosen up more, be more energetic, when we make love?"

Softer, but starting in with "Why don't you..." already makes for heavy criticism. The implication is, "As things are now, you don't measure up." It invites defensiveness on Bill's part.

"You're an excellent lover, Bill, but I do wish you'd be more vigorous when we're making love."

Cagey. Vicky wants to blunt criticism with praise, but this is confusing. If he's so excellent, how come the criticism? His options are: to view the praise as phony, to concentrate on the praise and blot out the criticism, to let the two parts of the message cancel each other out. There's little encouragement for a genuine dialogue to develop.

"I love you very much and I love being close to you when we're making love, Bill. But you're so gentle I don't feel as much as I might if you were more vigorous. I wonder how it strikes you?

It's all there. Vicky spoke for herself, backed up what she had to say, asked for feedback. Criticism is implied, but she has really put herself into the statement, suffused it with her own warmth and humanity. Naturally, there's no law that says Bill can't still take it amiss, but it's her best chance of reaching him, especially if she persists on being confronting. Let's follow through a bit on the way the dialogue could evolve:

Vicky: I love you very much and I love being close to you when we're making love, Bill. But you're so gentle I don't feel as much as I might if you were more vigorous. I wonder how it strikes you?

Bill: Funny you should be complaining about that. A lot of women complain that the men they're having sex with are much too rough.

Vicky: Well, I'm hardly one of them.

And that's hardly being confronting. If she wanted to keep the dialogue open, instead of closing it off like that, she might have said:

Vicky: I think I've made you angry. I hear it in your tone. And I really feel badly about that. I just want us to be as happy in all ways as we can.

Bill: I thought we were happy.

Vicky: Oh dear, when you get that look on your face and that tone in your voice, I feel so helpless, you know?

Bill: Well, you sprang this on me so suddenly. I thought everything was okay.

Vicky: I should have spoken up sooner, but this kind of conversation isn't easy for me so I kept postponing it. I hope you understand that.

Bill (*grudgingly*): Well, it isn't easy for me, either.

Bill isn't exactly being confronting yet, but he has come a long way from his initial closed-off stance. Actually, he has been putting more and more of himself into his retorts; so, almost in spite of himself, he's being drawn into a sympathetic and exploratory talk. Even though he's still hurt, in effect he's saying, "I share this feeling with you."

It's a big step in the direction of problem-solving.

9

Carrying On a Sexual Negotiation

HOW NOT TO NEGOTIATE

To negotiate, the dictionary says, is "to treat with another ... in order to come to terms or reach an agreement." It's self-evident that "treating" can be a highly useful tool in several kinds of situations common to the sex lives of many couples, namely:

—Where one partner wants to try a specific sexual position and the other doesn't.

—Where one partner wants to try a specific sexual technique and the other doesn't.

—Where one partner wants the other to perform a specific sexual act and the other refuses.

Any such situation is ready-made for arguments and tears, for each partner can easily become outraged by the other's attitude, feel put upon, and build up resentments that are destructive to the relationship.

People who want something in the sexual area but are denied by their partners often go on to act in ways that may, to them, have the look of negotiation but are actually self-defeating patterns of behavior:

They become accusing. Like children who can't get their own way, many men and women (men especially) flare up when they learn that their lovers or spouses won't grant them their wishes. Even some persons who would ordinarily champion another's right to say no somehow put sex in a special category and become furious at being denied what they want. This prompts them to make a personal attack, usually something like, "You're inadequate," or, "You're frigid," or, "You're a lousy lay"—a remark that denigrates the other's sexuality.

This is nasty. It's also unproductive, because it simply invites the other to be vituperative in turn. To have shot back at one, "You're a lousy lay, too!" can be as disconcerting to oneself as the original indignity was to the other.

They become legalistic. This pattern usually begins with the partner whose sexual request has been denied saying, "I have a right to it," or, "I have a right to it because you're my spouse." The other responds with, "I have just as much right to say no."

It's the legalistic approach to a relationship, each partner measuring out "rights" like so many dispensations being issued at the bar of justice. Not only is this antithetical to intimacy and openness, nothing gets accomplished: both partners have "rights" so the two rights cancel each other out.

They use sheer persuasion. Also a very poor tactic. "Convincing" somebody to do something usually is tantamount to coercing him. And coercion leads to reprisals and has the potential of damaging the couple's overall relationship. For example, a husband wants to be fellated once a week. His wife says no. He works on her and works on her until finally, wearily, she gives in. She fellates him but hates it and boils over with resentment toward him because she feels she's being used. Eventually she retaliates: by "forgetting" things, nagging him, belittling him in front of company, or taking unto herself a sympathetic lover who doesn't make her do such (to her) nasty things.

So much for the partner who wants to try something new and is turned down. The partner to whom the request is made also has a responsibility not to communicate destructively. If you've been asked to go along with a sexual technique you find unappealing or even repugnant, keep these pointers in mind:

1. Don't be mad at your partner for asking; asking's not a crime.

2. Don't just say no and expect the matter to be dropped. The logical rejoinder to "no" is "why not?" Any request merits discussion.

3. Don't show contempt or ridicule for the proposed idea; just because it's not your cup of tea doesn't mean thousands of others aren't drinking it.

4. Don't snap, "That's abnormal!" In large measure sexual abnormality, like beauty, is in the eye of the beholder. (From a mental-health point of view only the more extreme sadomasochistic exercises, fetishes, and forcible rape are likely to be called abnormal these days.)

For both the partner who seeks new delights and the one who doesn't think they're so delightful, the confronting approach is the one that can bridge their differences. Forcing both partners to be open rather than judgmental, to explore their own feelings rather than psych each other, to negotiate rather than argue, it can generate the understanding and sympathy that are vital elements to a successful resolution.

USING CONFRONTATION TO NEGOTIATE

Let's take a fairly common marital conflict: Husband and wife have been married a few years and they're getting along all right, but now the husband wants them to really do something they've only made half-hearted stabs at in the past. He wants them to add to their repertoire what's currently very much in vogue, mutual oral-genital sex. She says nothing doing, she doesn't like it. He stews about it silently for a few days, then decides to have a talk with her. He's going to try to negotiate.

Here's the way a first confronting talk might go:

Husband: I'm really upset that you're so dead set against it. I wish we could be so free with each other that we could do anything. Do you know what I mean?

Wife: Yes, but when you say that you want me to do *that* with you—well, it makes me feel you don't have any respect for me. And when I think you don't have any respect for me I really get angry at you.

Husband: Well, it could seem like a lack of respect. But I want it to be mutual.

Wife: But I don't enjoy it.

Husband: All right, I'll talk just about my side of it. What it really means to me doesn't have anything to do with respect. I would enjoy it, but also, it would mean to me that you really care for me, that my penis is important to you—

Wife: It is important to me but I just can't understand why that's the way I have to prove it. I don't understand why doing that is so important for you.

Husband: Like I said, I get a lot of pleasure out of it. And when you don't want to do it, it makes me feel you're rejecting me.

Wife: I don't mean to reject you, that's not my intention at all. But I just can't do it, it repulses me.

And that's about where, for the moment, the talk should probably end. Otherwise they're apt to go around in circles. Actually, much more has been accomplished than it might seem on the surface. Both have tried to be open and to relate the talk to their inner feelings. Both have avoided being aggressive and have really tried to explain themselves to and understand each other. The husband especially has put himself on the line. The wife hasn't been able to be that open yet. But that she hasn't, and that this talk hasn't resolved anything, is unimportant. They've spotlighted a sensitive issue and shown trust and concern in dealing with it.

So where are they in the negotiation? Both have difficult tasks ahead. The wife has the task of truly reaching into her emotions for the reasons why she can't participate in oral sex with her husband. The husband has the task of accepting things as they are for the time being. He may, of course, be very impatient to get the thing settled. As social worker Ron Brazman points out, people have a tendency to want sexual desires gratified at once, in contrast to other desires they're willing to defer.

"It's as though sexual feelings are more special than other feelings, and that's because those feelings are concretely tied to being a man or a woman," he says.

But in actuality sexual feelings aren't more special and the man has to wait to give his wife a chance to come to grips with the problem his request has created for her. Of course, the longer he's kept dangling the more likely it is he'll begin to feel somehow cheated. Soon they'll have to talk again. The situation being what it is, he'll probably have to initiate that second talk.

In the confronting spirit he might say:

Husband: I've been doing a lot of thinking about this. I know how difficult it is for you, and if it weren't so important to me I'd drop it right away. But I do feel rejected when you say you're repulsed by it because I guess I feel very strongly that my penis *is* me, in a way. So somehow what I'm left with is that you're repulsed by me.

Wife: I wish I could convince you that the one thing has nothing to do with the other. You're not repulsive to me, not in any way. I love you. I want and need you. Will you believe that?

Husband: I do—but there's that other feeling, too. And there's something else. We've begun talking about this thing now. It's out in the open and I think we should deal with it. When we don't it's like unfinished business to me. Like I'm being left hanging, waiting. I really would like to have us talk seriously about this. I really want to understand why you feel the way you do. Do you understand what's going on with me?

She does, but whether she can explore her own emotions

with him now is another question. However, if he keeps on being open, understanding, and supportive, chances are good that during either this talk or another she'll really open up.

RESOLUTION

The essence of confronting communication is a striving for growth and change, a striving for greater intimacy. But one person can't change another. The best either can do is to generate the kind of atmosphere in which they may express themselves freely and mutually. Sometimes an exploration of attitudes really does lead a resistant partner to have a change of heart. When it happens it usually does so because this partner gradually learns, "I don't have to be afraid. Nobody is judging me. I don't have to feel guilty about doing this."

When it occurs this way, a happy ending for everybody concerned, it's wonderful—and the confronting kind of approach gives it the best chance of happening. But neither that approach nor any other can guarantee its happening. The resistant partner may be unable to hurdle the emotional blocks that keep him or her from agreeing to the other's request. Sometimes not even complete openness and candidness on the one hand, and utter gentleness and understanding and support on the other, are enough to do away with those blocks. Shocking, traumatic early life experiences may be responsible; some women who can't bear to engage in fellatio, for instance, recall having been forced during childhood to fellate a man.

So an impasse may be reached. What then? It's a fallacy to assume that talk—even the most honest and feeling kind of talk—will necessarily lead to changed behavior. When they start out talking, one partner often wrongly assumes a change will eventually occur in the thinking of the other—and feel hurt and let down if it doesn't. Be fair. Be realistic. Be open-minded about the outcome.

And where does that leave the person who wants to try something new but even after negotiation is left with the answer "no"?

Well, if I want to engage in a particular technique, say, and you simply can't go for that one, I have some choices. I can try to force you, nourish a grudge, seek someone else to have that pleasure with—or evaluate the situation in terms of you and me.

If our overall relationship is a good one and I decide upon evaluation, then I must weigh whether it means more to me to engage in the technique than to acquiesce to the force of your need not to engage in it. If I conclude that it doesn't mean as much to me—then that's it, the matter's dropped, let's come up with something else that we can both enjoy together. I accept your need to refuse because I accept your right to your own likes and dislikes, your right to be different from me.

But if despite the intensity of your feelings mine are equally intense and I just have to engage in that technique, then I'm faced with a new issue—myself. There's a considerable repertoire of sexual activities available to us; why then am I so hung up on this one? What does this one really mean to me, aside from erotic pleasure? Am I involved in a power struggle with you? Does this technique have a special significance to me that I haven't fully acknowledged or recognized? Wherever that line of questioning takes me, if I'm ruthlessly honest with myself, I'll discover something new about myself. And whatever it is I discover is apt to lessen my need for the technique in question.

Paradoxically, a sexual negotiation that is worked out through confrontation can have a positive resolution for both partners even if one is denied a wish. They've discussed a sensitive subject frankly and warmly (albeit with a little heat, too); they've gotten more inside themselves and each other. So the talk is a success in this sense: it has raised the level of intimacy between them.

10

How to Avoid Three Common Communications Traps

CHECK OUT SEXY SIGNALS

Probably no other ordinary human endeavor prompts us to be as cryptic as many of us are in sex. Signs, signals, half-veiled messages, euphemisms—all abound. One person's "Want to do something tonight, dear?" said with a special intonation is as eloquent as another person's "Want to screw?" (And probably a good deal more acceptable.) Yet there's a big problem with signs, signals, and euphemisms: they can easily lend themselves to being misread. Therapists and marriage counselors report that this happens not infrequently. Even long-married couples that relate comfortably and have established a pattern of sexy signals sometimes fall into the trap.

Take Janet, who wears sexy nightgowns when she has a mind for sex; this is her signal, the one her husband picks up. But every so often she likes to wear a sexy nightgown just for the fun of it, not because sex is on her mind. Then, when he tries, she turns him down. This confuses and annoys him; sometimes the result is a tiff. Janet maintains he should know instinctively when the signal is a signal and when it isn't.

Take Helen, whose way of announcing she wants sex is to

declare to her husband, "I'm going to take a bath now, dear."
He knows that when she emerges from the bathroom she'll be
freshly bathed, powdered, perfumed—and expectant. Since
they've restricted themselves to this kind of cryptic communication, he feels duty-bound (and ego-bound) to perform even
when he's not really in the mood. This is beginning to take its
toll, for he's starting to have trouble maintaining his potency.

Then there's the hello-darling-I'm-home-from-work kiss, a
routine which can lead to an awful lot of confusion when one
partner sees the kiss as affectional and the other as sexual, or
when both aren't quite sure *what* is being conveyed with it.
Some men and women who have this communication problem
eventually find it easier to skip the kiss altogether.

After talking separately to a husband and wife who were
going through this kind of conflict, I jotted down the essential
thoughts of each that seemed to typify their dilemma:

Wife: "If I kiss him when he comes home he'll think it's a
sign I want to make love, and I don't.

"If I don't kiss him, he'll think I'm rejecting him.

"If I kiss him and turn away he'll think I'm just teasing, and
that's liable to get him angry.

"If I give him a quick hug instead, he's liable to grab me
anyway.

"I think I'll just be lying down with a headache when he
comes in."

Husband: "If she kisses me it's a sign she wants me to make
love to her, and I've had too hard a day in the office to want it.

"If I don't respond to her kiss, she'll think I'm angry about
something—or don't love her any more.

"If I kiss her and let it go at that she'll think something is
the matter with me.

"If I just give her a squeeze and turn away, she's liable to
think I'm angry or cold or something, too.

"I think I'll just work late tonight."

These two people had gotten themselves especially tangled

up in knots, but their exaggerated situation illustrates the kind of thing that happens more often than might be expected.

If in some minds Kiss = Sex, the equation Erection = Sex is even more likely. As Dr. William Hartman points, out, there are men who can get an erection any time they hug or kiss a woman, can get it four or five or six times a day, and not necessarily want to make love. The erection may simply be a physical way of saying, "I really go for you," rather than, "I need to have sex with you right now."

When couples don't recognize this alternative, they may feel compelled to have sex whether or not they really want it. This is a fairly common occurrence. Look at a striking case handled by a family service agency in Minnesota. Married seventeen years, a couple was showing markedly little affection. The wife was especially distant; her husband assumed she didn't love him any more. The truth is that he happened to be one of those men who do get erections very quickly and easily; his wife wrongly assumed that whenever it happened he wanted sex. So, even if she wasn't so inclined, she began making sexual overtures; he responded sexually to *her* overtures; and so it went. Finally she avoided even putting her arms around him for fear of stirring up an erection. Given the fact that they never actually talked about any of this, it's not surprising that their problems escalated.

An even more common assumption is that foreplay has to lead to intercourse. The result is that couples that might have a perfectly good time just playing feel obliged to follow through because—well, because each partner thinks that that's what's expected. I know a man who's beginning to feel oppressed by his new girl friend because every time they kiss and pet she abruptly excuses herself and goes into the bathroom to put on a diaphragm. (It's the only birth control method she can use.) Then the man feels he has to have sex with her regardless of his own mood; not to have it under the circumstances would, to him, be a reflection on his manhood. Since he and she haven't discussed the matter he has no way of knowing whether she feels under compulsion, too, and whether that's the reason she always makes her move to put on her diaphragm.

Sexy signals have their place but it's pretty chancy to rely on them exclusively. Try not to guess at a signal; if you're not sure, ask. Don't assume your own signal will always be understood as you want it to be; clarify it. If necessary, get feedback. A signal is a signal, not a coercive device; if you feel yourself coerced, either by your partner or by your own inner workings, this might be the time for an open, confronting talk.

In sum, signals are a kind of shorthand many of us use, but at times there's no substitute for spelling things out.

AVOID SEXUAL DOUBLE-TALK

When you're double-talking, you're sending out what in communications parlance is called a "double-bind message." That means you're sending out two messages at once, one the direct opposite of the other. Typically, when you're double-talking you're saying one thing with words and conveying something else again by other words—or by tone, inflection, look, stance, gesture, or other nonverbal sign. This has the obvious result of confusing the recipient of your two messages, and confusion often leads to conflict. When people send out double-bind messages, however, they usually aren't aware of it.

Sex lends itself readily to the double-bind trap because it's so emotional a subject and because people haven't defined their emotions about it with great clarity. In other words, their own confusion prompts them to talk in confusing double-talk.

Sherod Miller, an expert in interpersonal communications at the University of Minnesota, makes an excellent point about sexual double-talk: society itself is the very paradigm of it. On the one hand, society says, "Be spontaneous about sex, let yourself go." On the other hand, society says, "Be orderly, be in control, operate your life according to time segments and schedules." So we come home in the evening, many of us, and schedule thirty minutes for spontaneous sex.

There are plenty of other homespun examples of sexual double-talk from which to choose. The kind of person who in an earlier day was called a "tease" blatantly engages in that kind of talk. At one and the same time such a person says:

"Come and get me."

"Hands off."

Sexual double-talk is often prompted by a partner's ambivalence with regard to having sex. Here are three typical—and maybe familiar—examples:

Husband: Honey, are you in the mood tonight?
Wife (*eyes sparkling*): Mmmmmm . . .
Husband: Good.

But when it's near bedtime he switches on the television set and settles down to watch the late night movie.

Wife: Darling, are you going to show me a good time tonight?
Husband (*eyes sparkling*): And how!
Wife (*as bedtime approaches*): I've got a headache.

Wife (*wiggling against her husband*): How do you feel . . . ?
Husband (*responding*): You know how I feel . . .
Wife: Shall we . . . ?
Husband: You bet!
Wife (*as they're about to make love*): How come we hardly ever have sex?

This hits him like a cold shower, of course. So instead of making love they talk, and quarrel, and don't have sex that night either. Which is what, underneath it all, the wife wanted to have happen in the first place.

You can see how persons receiving a double-bind message

really are in a bind. First they're hit with one message, then with the other, and they don't know what to do. For that matter, whatever they do is wrong.

Take the man whose wife at first wants sex and then winds up with a headache. If he says to himself, "Okay, she's got a headache, I won't try anything," he feels cheated because he has been led to anticipate sex. If he says to himself, "I don't care if she's got a headache, I'm going to follow through," he feels guilty—or is made to feel guilty.

Most often people don't know precisely that they're sending or receiving double-bind messages, but when it happens telltale signs are likely to occur:

1. There's confusion in the air.

2. An undertone of anger manifests itself.

3. The receiver of the double message is liable to feel helpless.

4. The receiver may act in ways contrary to the sender's intentions.

5. The receiver is likely to feel or say, "How come I can never please you? How come I'm always guessing wrong about you?"

6. The receiver may suddenly become very persuasive in reacting to the sender, as if to say, "You're not really giving me an idea of what you want, so I'm going to try to convince you to do what I want."

If one or more of these signs lead you to suspect that you're talking sexual double-talk, take stock. Try to step outside yourself when you talk sex to your partner; see if there's something about the way you act that belies the words you say, or something about the words that belies your actions. Look for any contradictions or inconsistencies between your talk and your behavior, or between what you say at one point and what you say at another. If you do spot a double message of yours, you've already come a long way toward eliminating the practice. Think both parts of that message through. Ask yourself which part you *really* mean—and why you sent both. The way to talk straight is to gain some understanding as to why you had to be confusing.

And if you're the target for sexual double-talk, what are your alternatives? There really aren't any; there's just one truly workable step you can take. And that step is to get to the heart of the issue, too, the double-bind message itself. Go over any contradictions and inconsistencies on your partner's part in your mind until you've isolated the two halves of the double message. Then you can show your partner the two halves and, in effect, ask, "Which one of these would you like me to act upon?" Hopefully your partner will recognize what's been happening and give you a straight answer. But that may not happen. No recognition may come. In that case, try to convey how you feel when you are the target for a double message. In other words, metacommunicate. At the very least, your awareness of the trap and how it works can make it a less onerous one.

TAKE RESPONSIBILITY FOR YOUR SEXUAL SELF

Many people expect something impossible from their sexual partners: they expect them to be mind readers. They expect their partners to "understand"—by intuition or osmosis or whatever—what it is they like and don't like in regard to sex.

"When two people really love each other," one lady of around thirty told me, "they can dispense with words. Their closeness is enough. It allows them to respond to each other, to cater to each other's needs. The closer they are the more intuitive they become about each other."

Intuition is a wonderful thing, all the more so when two people are so emotionally attuned to each other that they have a genuine feel for each other's feelings; but some people are more intuitive than others. In any event, intuition is hardly the most reliable form of communication for everyday use.

When one person expects another person to intuit his needs and desires he's being dreadfully unfair to the other because he's placing all that burden upon the other. What he's saying is, "It's not my job to speak about my needs and desires, it's your job to know what they are." The corollary to that is, "I'm not taking any responsibility for my own communication—or for my own satisfaction." And the final logical step in this sequence of thinking is, "If you don't know what I need, it's your fault, not mine."

The person who thinks that way is always off the hook; if things go wrong he can always blame his partner for having let him down. It should come as no surprise that the pattern leads to the casting of blame, to misunderstandings, to resentments— and to unsatisfactory sex.

The reason it's a destructive pattern is that it's rooted not in some lofty notions about love but in the wish to be dependent. "The idea that one should always know what the other is feeling mirrors a parent-child kind of relationship," Dr. Ruth Aaron observes. "The good parent is tuned into her child, feels responsible for knowing if the child is irritated, frightened, tired, or what have you. And the child comes to expect that from the parent."

The child does, but one definition of adulthood is to have outgrown that kind of dependency, to assume responsibility for oneself and one's needs. Sooner or later relationships founded on dependency generate a lot of anger; the dependent person is angry for having to be dependent, the other for having the burden of responsibility placed upon him.

In sum, if you want to be tickled or pressed or licked in a certain way, there's really no effective substitute for speaking up and asking; if you don't want to be tickled in a certain place, or a particular caress makes you uncomfortable, or there's an experiment you'd rather not try, nothing takes the place of saying so. Verbal intimacy belongs with physical intimacy.

So much for taking *too little* responsibility for one's sexual self. Taking *too much* responsibility for one's partner's sexual satisfaction is just as destructive.

To be sure, most marriage manuals and much popular thinking about sex is grounded in the viewpoint that each partner "should" please the other; that each has the task of sexually satisfying the other. On the face of it this notion of reciprocity has compelling appeal: I make you happy, you make me happy; having given to each other we drift off on a cloud of sexual contentment. The trouble with this notion is that, at bottom, it's a kind of misguided unselfishness that easily causes a lot of mischief, to wit:

If you and I are having sex and I begin with the attitude, "This isn't going to be any good unless I make you happy," I'm literally assuming all of the responsibility for your sexual happiness. In the best of circumstances that's a tremendous load to take on, both psychologically and physiologically, and the less comfortable one feels about one's sexual adequacy the more of a load it becomes.

If I assume all of the responsibility for your sexual happiness I give you a passive role in relation to that happiness; in effect I say that I'll do all the work for you.

If I assume all of the responsibility for your sexual happiness, I'm doing something very risky in terms of my ego: I'm saying my worth is based on your satisfaction. Then, if things aren't all that great, my ego has gotten quite a blow.

If I assume all of the responsibility for your sexual happiness, what about mine? Either I give it short shrift and sooner or later feel cheated, or I expect you to assume all of the responsibility for *my* sexual satisfaction and if things aren't that wonderful I begin to resent you.

None of this is to say we shouldn't want to please each other sexually, only to say that if this is our basic intent it tends to lead to trouble. The alternative? Call it a kind of enlightened selfishness. Very simply, we each take responsibility for our own sexual satisfaction. It doesn't mean we don't care about each other's—of course we do—just that we're not weighted down by that feeling of "I've *got* to make you happy."

Enlightened selfishness assumes we're both mature enough to take responsibility for ourselves; that we'll both *do* what we can to give ourselves as much pleasure as we can; that we'll both *tell* each other what we want done, what's pleasing, what isn't—in effect, that we'll both be fully functioning participants in our lovemaking.

11

Quarrels and Sex, Sex and Quarrels

TO FIGHT OR NOT TO FIGHT?

There are couples who say, "We never fight." They don't fight about sex, about anything. On the surface, at least, they have no conflicts.

Such couples don't usually go on to say, "We never have sex," but this is what very often seems to happen. Professionals working with troubled families often find a strong connection between lack of fighting and lack of sex. Self-styled "all-loving" couples, explains clinical psychologist Dr. Israel Charny, don't show much passion in any facet of their relationships.

"In my experience they relate like two old friends, or two aunts together," he says. "They have a real fear of confronting each other around issues—playing it safe like crazy—and the price for playing it safe is that they can't experience that whole flow of passion."

Though separateness and risk are part of any genuine emotional tie, the we-never-fight couples try to build a whole world together in which separateness and risk won't be part of the experience. Theirs is a paradox: they're both uniquely together and uniquely apart. Their lackluster or nonexistent sex life doesn't bother them—at least outwardly; when they seek clinical help it's for another reason—a problem child, for instance. Outwardly they're placid; whatever tensions exist underneath—and they do exist—these men and women try never to rock the boat.

Yet conflict is an inevitable aspect of any relationship marked by health and growth. No matter how well we've mastered communications techniques or how close and loving we are, we and our partners are always involved with elements that invite disagreement and quarrels from time to time. Elements like dialogue, debate, the airing of issues, the search for compromise. As we assert ourselves, explosions inevitably occur.

In a larger sense, moreover, any emotional relationship is characterized both by love and by hate—two extreme emotions, Dr. Charny suggests, in whose natural flow we're always caught. It's the tensions between these two opposing forces that make a close relationship bearable, enabling the two partners to join together for sex and other pleasures.

WHY PEOPLE FIGHT ABOUT SEX

Quarrels and sex have a number of elements in common. Quarrels imply an outburst, an explosion; sexual intercourse ends with a physical explosion of sorts. Though they may have been brewing awhile, quarrels come to life suddenly; while there's a gradual buildup to orgasm, its arrival too is marked by a startling suddenness. Quarrels can promote intimacy; sex is an act of great intimacy. Quarrels are emotional reactions; sex is about as emotion-laden an act as we can engage in. Quarrels express feelings, often violently; sex can certainly do the same. Both quarrels and sex can be used to avoid facing issues, stir up excitement, or relieve inner stress.

Some people have a rousing good fight every once in a while

just for the pleasure of making up in bed; there are also people whose sex life flowers only after bitter quarreling. Some people fight because it's really the only way they know how to settle things or because they consistently fail to employ the proper communications techniques. Fights often occur because it's an effective way of deflating tension that has built up over some issue.

As for quarrels specifically related to sex, we can break these down into five major categories:

1. A straightforward sex fight. The two partners have a specific disagreement about sex and quarrel about it.

2. An indirect sex fight. A partner is angry about something related to sex but shows it by picking a fight about a nonsexual issue, like the wife who wants more sex but screams at her husband for leaving his clothes lying around. She can't bring herself to face the sexual issue directly.

3. Sex as a scapegoat. The reverse of No. 2; a partner is angry about something nonsexual but picks a fight on sexual grounds. For instance, a husband can't stand his mother-in-law and takes it out on his wife by quarreling with her about their infrequent sex activity.

4. A sexual cover-up. This is when the fight ostensibly is about one sexual issue while the basic conflict has to do with another sexual issue, as when a husband berates his wife for not being more interested in sex when he's really angry that she won't fellate him. He has his own hangups about fellatio or he'd tackle the problem directly.

5. The fight as a cover-up. In this one a partner who doesn't want sex but is expected to have it picks a fight about anything, anything at all; he succeeds in making his partner angry and thus eliminates the threat of sex.

There's still another way of looking at quarrels, from the widest perspective of all. Psychoanalyst Warren L. Jones offers a provocative view, dividing all fights, sexual and otherwise, into three distinct patterns—patterns that reflect the overall relationship.

The first pattern is *dependency*. Regardless of the specific issue, the struggle, which may be either the overt or covert, is about who's going to do the giving and who's going to do the taking in the relationship. Dependency is the name of the game: like babies, each partner wants to be *the* one nurtured, catered to, taken care of.

The second pattern is a struggle for *power*. "In this category each partner is striving to dominate the other, to get the upper hand, to have control of the situation," says Dr. Jones. "Whether the relationship is polite and slick on the surface or whether it's rough and crude, the quarrels in essence are a power struggle."

Sex often becomes a vehicle for the attempt at domination; one partner often uses it to dominate, manipulate, or tear down the other.

The third pattern has to do with *sharing*. Ironically, even when the relationship is characterized by sharing, by cooperation and equality, quarrels can erupt. In fact, they erupt precisely because the partners are used to give-and-take—and then they encounter some situation in which it seems to one as if this mutuality is being given short shrift. For instance, a husband wants sex, his wife doesn't; she mistakes his eagerness for insistence and coercion; she's outraged; he's outraged at her outrage; the battle is joined. They fight, they clear the air, trust is reestablished.

All this makes it clear that fights are much more complicated than they might seem to be. To get the most out of your sex fights—that is, to gain a release and resolution—you have to have some idea of what you're fighting about. There are signs that reveal when fights aren't accomplishing these ends:

—Your fights never seem to get anywhere; you go round and round and round, and the air isn't cleared.

—You come away from a fight feeling you haven't really had your say.

—Your fights don't provide you with a feeling that you've really unburdened yourself.

If so, review your quarrels in light of the patterns outlined here. Also, during a quarrel use one part of your mind to step outside yourself, to hear yourself talk. Are you speaking straight—or do the words sound phony or incomplete, as if you're holding something back? You may not want to say everything you feel, not in the heat of the moment, but listening to yourself can help tell you whether you're anywhere near the true source of the conflict. Finally, discuss the problem of ineffectual fighting with the partner with whom you're doing the fighting. Unless you're both interested in quarreling for its own sake, you'll both want to identify the nature of the fight, thereby clearing the way for a satisfying resolution.

FIGHTING FOUL AND FAIR

Quarrels about sex, as about anything else, can be fought destructively or constructively. Even if the two of you know exactly what you're fighting about, a battle can render the atmosphere heavy with bitterness; it all depends on the way you fight.

If you don't want to fight foul:

—*Don't* make sarcastic, belittling, or insulting remarks about your partner's sexual adequacy. It's a mean and dirty way to fight, it generates powerful resentments—and leaves you open to similar hurts.

—*Don't* invoke the names of former spouses, lovers, mistresses, or assorted boy friends or girl friends to prove how much happier your sexual experiences were with them than with your present partner. It's belittling, it sets up a kind of malicious triangle situation—and, again, two can play the game.

—*Don't* play amateur psychologist, clinically scrutinizing your partner's personality or sex life. It's a put-down even if you're convinced you're "helping." Chances are you'll be way off in terms of accurately assessing your partner—but even if you're not, you're the last person in the world your partner wants this kind of help from, especially during a quarrel.

—*Don't* threaten to tell your parents all about the issue surrounding the fight, and don't threaten to run home to them. Invoking your parents' names is a way of ganging up on your partner. Besides, that's what children do, and you're not a child any more—are you?

—*Don't* bring your own children into the argument, even if they're old enough to understand the ramifications involved. You're likely to wreak emotional havoc when you involve them in your sex life on such a personal level—and when you force them to take sides for one parent against the other.

If you want to fight fair:

—*Do* be as clear as you can about your grievances, rather than keeping your partner guessing.

—*Do* be forthright about your feelings, about your anger. You have a right to your feelings; anger is nothing to be ashamed of.

—*Do* listen to your partner as well as to yourself, rather than simply preparing your retort while your partner is speaking.

—*Do* be honest in admitting it if your partner scores a telling point. A successful fight, after all, clarifies issues rather than proving a person right or wrong.

SEXUAL FINALES

The sexual equivalent of "Let's kiss and make up" obviously is "Let's fuck and make up," more politely known as "sexual consolation."

Under some circumstances nothing is more natural, more apt to promote a feeling of sexual hunger and emotional well-being. Here we are, having just had an outburst, an exchange of angry words. But the anger and the words have helped us to understand each other better, and have also helped to bridge the momentary coldness between us that preceded the fight. Now we feel warm and close. We want to express these feelings and we want reassurance that everything is all right again.

Making love is a beautiful way of accomplishing all this.

Sometimes. Sometimes, though, the sexual finale to a quarrel isn't all that positive. If quarrels aren't resolved, if issues are left hanging, making up in bed can simply be a way of dodging the issues—hiding behind sex to avoid coming to grips with them. If that happens occasionally, it's a matter of small importance. If it's a habitual way of dealing with problems it's destructive. It's destructive because nothing is solved: the problems pile up. Sooner or later the sexual relationship also is affected; at that point it's even beyond the capacity of sex to soothe the wounds.

What often happens is that one partner wants to use sex to make up, while the other partner flatly rejects the idea. Men more than women are prone to want to forgive and forget in the bedroom; women more frequently seem not to like the idea at all. The partner who declines may still be angry; may be continuing the fight by refusing to have sex, a form of one-upmanship; or may genuinely view sex as an unsatisfactory, unrealistic approach to problem-solving, and hope to try for a resolution on a more mature and realistic basis.

12

Confession Is Good for the Soul —Sometimes

PREMARITAL AND MARITAL: SHOULD PARTNERS TELL?

Tell about what? About their previous sex experiences, of course. We can dispose of that one with little trouble. It depends on the two people involved. On their background, sophistication, and emotional state. It's as inappropriate for a lady who has a romantic alliance with a conservative male to trot out all her previous affairs as it is for a lady who travels in sexually sophisticated circles to avoid all mention of her sex life.

Sexual sophistication, however, provides no absolute guarantee against untoward reactions in the face of a sexual revelation. Just as would-be swingers sometimes fail to enjoy the swinging scene because of one or both partners' jealousy, so a revelation of "I've had it, I've enjoyed it" sometimes creates havoc even when the two partners involved take it for granted they didn't enter their relationship as virgins.

In a classic paper on sex and power, Dr. Seymour L. Halleck of the University of Wisconsin has described a case of this kind. A liberal young husband and wife launched into a discussion of premarital sex. The wife told her husband for the first time about a brief premarital affair she had engaged in shortly before her marriage, one she had enjoyed tremendously. Her husband shrugged it off. Soon after, though, he began to insist upon having sex with her every single night. This eventually caused so much conflict they were forced to seek professional help.

In effect, this husband had become highly competitive with the ghost of a lover past! Of course, the wife may have presented her experience in such a way as to trigger his insecurities. *How* something is revealed is as important as *what* is revealed. And the how depends on the *why*. What's the reason for making the revelation? Honesty is one thing, cruelty is another. What may seem like an attempt to be open and honest about one's previous sexual experiences may, underneath, be an attempt to hurt or antagonize the other. Before baring your past history to your present partner, examine your motivations.

In the normal course of a relationship, the better a man and woman know each other the more freely they discuss their sexual histories. Each new generation shows less reticence about that; the emphasis is on honesty. (Honesty to a degree: in the past some women pretended to a virginity they no longer had; now that sex is in, some women and men pretend to more experience than they've had. The ethics in either instance are equally questionable.) The more relevant question today is less whether to tell about previous affairs or experiences than how graphic to be about them.

Again, there's no single answer. Again, it depends on the two people involved. It also depends on the reasons why they want to tell about or listen to such accounts. Casual mentions that don't raise emotional heat are one thing; elaborate descriptions of what you did with whom and how it felt are another. Let's look at four sets of Jacks and Janes and at what prompts them to descriptive extremes:

Jack and Jane I exchange accounts of erotic experiences they have had with previous partners the way some couples exchange sexual fantasies—because it turns them on. It satisfies their voyeuristic wishes and has an aphrodisiac effect. It's a way they enjoy themselves.

Jack and Jane II talk in rich detail about previous sex experiences as a way of really saying to each other, "Look how experienced I am!" Of course, it doesn't have to be mutual. Just one may do the boasting, forcing the other to listen. And the boast can be in the spirit of "I've been around!" or "I'm better than you!"

Jack III tells Jane III all about what he did with previous girl friends because he knows it's going to get her all upset, and he enjoys seeing her upset. Obviously, this can work the other way around, too, with Jane III telling Jack III all there is to tell about her sex history because she enjoys seeing him squirm. The question is why the one on the receiving end submits to this instead of simply saying, "I don't want to hear about it." Jack and Jane IV provide an answer.

Jack IV insists on hearing from Jane IV all the things she did with other men because he *wants* to suffer—or Jane IV takes it all in from Jack IV for the same reason. Now, in this situation, why does the one who's made to do the talking actually go ahead and talk in the face of the other's discomfiture? See Jack and Jane III for a possible solution.

If you and your partner are prone to tell "all," but wonder whether or not it's a good idea, the exploits of our various Jacks and Janes may prove instructive. In the end, two basic questions apply:

1. How do you feel about the revelations?
2. How does your partner feel about them?

Only you two can gauge how comfortable you really are when one or the other is telling all.

EXTRAMARITAL: OWNING UP WITHOUT SPEAKING UP

Some husbands and wives who make a habit of infidelity are remarkably adept at keeping their extramarital adventures a secret from their spouses; they're truly models of discretion. Some others tumble in and out of a single stranger's bed and blow the whole thing by leaving some telltale clue for their mates to find.

There are clues and clues. There are clues left accidentally, a bit of carelessness, a chance error. But often there's more to it than carelessness. That smudge of lipstick on the unfaithful husband's collar, the love note discovered in the wife's dresser drawer, the slip of the tongue that betrays the existence of a lover or mistress—often that seeming boner is a powerful form of communication, a way of saying, "Look, I'm cheating on you."

Call it a perverse form of confessing to infidelity. The partner who leaves clues under such circumstances may appear careless but on an unconscious level deliberately wants to be found out. There are good reasons why:

Guilt and expiation. "The weight of guilt some people feel about betraying their spouses is crushing," observes psychotherapist Oscar Rabinowitz. "They want to be relieved of that guilt, punished, set free. But they can't bring themselves to admit their infidelity openly so they leave clues for their mates to discover. Discovery leads to punishment. Once they're properly chastised they feel better."

For many persons this exorcism has a lasting effect. But others play out periodic extravaganzas of sin-suffer-and-repent with their mates. Both the mate who cheats and the mate who rages, punishes, and forgives derive gratification from this. Some people are born to suffer.

Hostility. An international airline pilot named Mike returned from a New York-Paris-New York flight with a reel of pornographic film, which he showed to his wife. Midway through the screening she uttered an exclamation and slapped him hard across the face. Though neither the two women nor the man in the film could be identified by their faces—they were wearing masks—she recognized Mike by a distinctive watch bracelet he was wearing. He'd forgotten to take it off.

Forgotten? Maybe. Since showing one's wife a porno movie in which one has had a starring role is in itself an act of great hostility, it's reasonable to suppose that on an unconscious level Mike's wearing of the telltale bracelet was also a deliberately hostile act.

In fact, leaving a clue to infidelity often is a way of saying to one's mate, "I want to hurt you"—all the more so if hostility provoked the infidelity in the first place. An angry spouse who takes revenge on his mate by sleeping with somebody else really doesn't gain the full satisfaction unless his mate becomes aware of what's happening. Dropping clues is an effective way of providing that awareness.

Infantile excitement. Barbie is a young wife who doesn't feel her day is worthwhile unless she has engaged in a mild flirtation, and who doesn't feel truly alive unless she's extra-maritally entangled. Her brief and furtive encounters give her a real psychic high. She's remarkably careless about her infidelities and often makes slips of the tongue or otherwise drops clues that require her to do a lot of explaining to her husband; she's constantly having to cover up.

Barbie says she likes to live dangerously but what's really involved is a need for a kind of infantile excitement. She feels her infidelities are wrong; the very fact that she does is what makes them so tantalizing. And the more dangerous the game becomes, as by leaving clues, the more exciting it becomes. People like Barbie want to put their head in the lion's mouth, so to speak, hoping they won't have it bitten off. When they're left intact, it proves to them that they really do have a head—in other words, proves to them that they're really somebodies, as sexual beings, as persons.

Termination. Some people want to end their affairs but don't want to face the unpleasantness involved. So they need somebody to help them, need a mommy or daddy to come to the rescue. Mommy or Daddy in this instance is the other spouse.

Edward, a junior executive with a nice family in the suburbs, illustrates the point. Edward has been having an affair with Penny, a secretary in his office. At first it was fun, but now Penny has become demanding and petulant; she wants him to divorce his wife and marry her. All Edward wants to do is be faithful to his wife again. So he tosses into a shirt drawer a love note Penny has written to him; his wife eventually finds it and forces him to make a break with Penny.

Sometimes the wronged spouse personally confronts the other man or woman and does the dirty work involved in effecting the break. This is even better for passive but disenchanted lovers.

It can work the other way, too. At times the unfaithful spouse wants to end the marital, not the extramarital, relationship. Unable to face his mate directly, he drops a few clues. His unconscious hope is that the mate will get the message, precipitate a crisis, and terminate the marriage for him. But this only works if the wronged mate is also just about ready to call it quits; in the judgment of most marriage counselors and therapists, adultery per se hardly ever prompts a divorce.

The leaving of clues can serve one or more of the purposes outlined here; whatever the purpose, though, it's self-evident that this is hardly the most honest form of communication. Whether it's meant to serve destructive or constructive ends, it's a sneaky way of accomplishing something.

In contrast to such indirect ways of owning up to unfaithfulness, there are . . .

REAL CONFESSIONS

It's often said that confession is good for the soul. It may well be—but just what does that soul have in mind? Sometimes a confession of infidelity, made openly and directly, is a positive step in a marital relationship. Sometimes it's a very negative one.

Why does an errant partner want to confess? There are parallels between the leaving of clues and the wish to confess. Hostility is one of the less noble motivations for wanting to make a clean breast of things. When a husband and wife are having a bitter quarrel and one of them blurts out a confession of infidelity, it's clear that angry, hostile impulses are at work. Similarly, it's hostility, the wish to hurt, that prompts a partner with suppressed anger toward his mate to become suddenly honest about an extramarital relationship. A marital fight may have occurred days before the revelation is made, but that doesn't mean leftover anger isn't a motivating force.

Panic and guilt can evoke a confession. Take Tony: his girl friend has been pushing him to get a divorce. He doesn't really want to and she threatens to confront his wife. Finally Tony faces his wife and blurts out the whole story—both to relieve himself of his guilt feelings and to get the psychic shove he needs to end the affair.

In some people guilt works the other way: they want to unburden themselves, but can't. "My mate will be crushed, will fall apart," they rationalize. Underneath, prompted by their guilt, is the real message from themselves to themselves: "I've done something terrible to my mate and if it's discovered my mate will do something terrible to me." But it's a self-defeating situation: their guilt piles up; they become depressed, resentful, difficult to live with, and usually wind up giving themselves away anyhow—either by leaving clues or by unexpectedly blurting out a confession.

A confession can, of course, be a way of trying to end the

marriage. Conversely, though it may not always be appreciated by the spouse on the receiving end, a confession can also be a way of trying to improve the marriage. People with marital problems often let things slide; they avoid facing up to and coping with their difficulties. Gradually the situation gets worse. One of the partners drifts into an affair, maybe to gratify some of the needs that aren't being gratified in the marriage. But then this same partner wakes up to what's happening, to the extent to which the marriage has deteriorated, and resolves to do something about it.

A confession under such circumstances becomes a more open way of saying, "There are things wrong here, things we're not getting to."

The confession that's made and accepted in the spirit of "Let's really look at what's happening to us and try to do something about it" can ultimately result in problems being faced and surmounted, in mates coming closer together.

Though most confessions are made spontaneously, on the spur of the moment, the wiser approach is to plan for it. That is, if constructive ends are hopefully to be achieved. If you want to confess to an extramarital relationship give some thought first to talking over the pros and cons with a knowledgeable professional, such as a marriage counselor. Otherwise:

—Examine your motives. Just what are you trying to accomplish by confessing? If the answer is, "To be honest," you're not being honest. Dig deeper.

—Choose a time when the home atmosphere isn't dense with conflict or anger; a confession made when anger is rife is an angry confession.

—Don't go into clinical detail about your extramarital sexual experiences. If you do talk about them, they can't help but hurt your partner and add to the strain of the situation. They can also boomerang later, when you might be trying to reestablish a sexual relationship with your spouse. Even if you're pressed for details, avoid the sexual specifics.

If your spouse confronts you with a clue to your infidelity, you have several choices. You can lie—and if your spouse *wants* to believe you innocent then any reasonable explanation or denial will suffice. You can admit the truth right then and there—but that may be tricky, especially if you and your mate are very emotional about the confrontation. Or you can try to postpone a serious talk, delaying a confession until both of you are calmer.

A word to people who are in the midst of an affair: it might be prudent to give some thought *now* to the way you'd handle things if your spouse ever confronted or accused you.

If you're in the other situation, a husband or wife who has found what seems to be evidence of your mate's infidelity, then:

—Don't jump to conclusions; you may be wrong about that evidence. A calm request for an explanation doesn't have the damaging consequences of a precipitous, angry reaction.

If you're sure the extramarital relationship exists, or if a confession has been made, you may feel very hurt and angry. You may want to take some hasty action just to relieve all that tension built up inside yourself, or to get back at your spouse. But some actions are self-destructive:

—*Don't* run home to your parents.

—*Don't* just pack up and move to a hotel or in with a friend.

—*Don't* try to throw the errant mate out of the house.

—*Don't* seek revenge by starting an affair of your own.

Difficult as it may be at the moment, *do* try to understand yourself a little better in relation to the infidelity before confronting your mate. It will help defuse your anger and enable you to deal more coolly and constructively with the painful situation. Ask yourself:

—Why am I hurt?

—Why am I angry?

—What does the episode really mean to me?

—What role may I have played in the situation?

You may find it helpful at this time to talk things over with an objective and knowledgeable outsider.

How to Talk
with
Significant Others

13

---

*The Children:
How to
Talk Sex
to Them*

EVERYBODY TALKS

Every single day parents talk to their children about sex. They do so even if they don't utter a single explicitly sexual word. The way a baby is held and bathed, the extent to which Dad involves himself in the child's upbringing, the style in which the children are dressed, the way the parents relate to each other and to the youngsters, the degree to which boy and girl children are regarded and treated differently, the rigidity or flexibility with which sex roles are played out in the family—all these and many other aspects of daily family life constitute part of the child's sex education.

So does the extent to which parents show tenderness, sentiment, and affection, explains Dr. Gregory T. Leville of the Family Service of Philadelphia. "Do the parents show affection to each other? Is it shown between all members of the family? Take a child who grows up in a home where there's very little if any affection expressed in front of the children, a home where there are no pats on the backside, no hugging, kissing, or whatever. This can have the effect that the child will never learn to use his body to express feeling and emotion. And using the body to express feeling and emotion is essential to sex," says Dr. Leville.

Though you can't expect yourself to be constantly aware of the multiple ways in which you talk sex to your children, it is well to remind yourself from time to time that the process is going on.

THE PARENT AS SEX EDUCATOR

Direct, explicit sex talk is something else again. You're perfectly aware that you're talking sex when you're talking it. But how well or badly are you coming across? How effective are you? That's not so easy to gauge. Dr. Robert A. Walsh of Illinois State University surveyed the sex attitudes of 750 freshmen and 1100 of their parents, and found that nearly three fourths of the fathers and two thirds of the mothers considered themselves the "major source" of their children's sex information. But only 7 percent of the young men and 29 percent of the young women themselves saw their parents in the same light. Looking back on it, most evaluated their parents' efforts at sex education as inadequate or worse.

Most other studies show similar results. They show that a minority of girls still aren't properly prepared even for menstruation and that shockingly few boys—hardly any, in fact—are told by either parent about the events they'll face at puberty: the production of semen, nocturnal emissions, and the like. Youngsters who reach puberty unaware of what physical changes and happenings they'll be going through often become fearful and feel shamed when those events take place. Parents' lack of skill as sex educators isn't limited to the time just preceding their children's adolescence, however, but reaches back to the early years. The fact is that it is far from easy for parents to talk to their children about sex, and there are a number of reasons why:

—Parents themselves aren't relaxed enough about sex to talk readily about it to their children.

—Parents tend to be emotional, rather than objective and insightful, about their own children's sex lives.

—Parents, even well-educated ones, tend to be surprisingly ill informed about the facts of human sexuality. They, too, were poorly taught about sex.

—The natural attraction that exists between parents and their children gets in the way.

One doesn't have to dwell on that erotic attraction, or believe in Freudian terms that a child wants the opposite-sex parent and sees the same-sex parent as a rival, to know it exists. Most families shrug it off, joke about it, or allude to it offhandedly ("My six-year-old boy, he treats me like a queen," one mother happily told others in a family life education program)—but the fact that it is there does contribute to an underlying embarrassment in parent-child sex talk.

For all these reasons a few sex-education experts think parents shouldn't talk to their children about sex at all. But theirs is an extreme position and not a very realistic one. Even when fine school or church sex-education programs are available to boys and girls, there are sound reasons for parents to discuss sex with their children. Parents can:

—Convey a sense of personal caring and concern.

—Convey their values about sex, which is very important because it fuels the children's own developing moral sense.

—Enhance family communication and intimacy when they and their children are able to talk about sex with some measure of trust.

—Avoid the artificiality and pretense that exists when everybody at home acts as though sex itself were nonexistent.

—Give sex the acceptability and status of normality that comes with making it a proper topic for discussion.

None of this is to suggest that every parent *must* engage in parent-child sex talk or, alternatively, shrivel up with guilt. If a parent feels acute discomfort in talking about sex, if the marital relationship is fraught with serious sex problems, or if talking about sex always seems to overstimulate the child, it's best for the parent not to pursue the subject. Some signs of sexual overstimulation in children are: sudden hostility, waking up at night, unpredictable or erratic behavior, more childish behavior, hyperactivity, frequent masturbation, and/or eagerness on the child's part to see his parents making love.

But even in such special situations, sex shouldn't be ignored; the child must still learn to cope with his own sex drive. Just as significant, the more explosive the subject is at home, the more curious and anxious the child is apt to feel about it. You can always encourage the youngster to discuss sex with knowledge-able and sensitive outsiders—a trusted relative, maybe, or a perceptive teacher or doctor. Sex-education books and pamphlets may also be helpful, but choose carefully; there are both excellent and poor materials on the market for children of all ages.

Special circumstances aside, you may find it awkward to talk about sex to your children for the same reason so many people find it awkward to talk about sex generally: a lack of the communication skills involved. The more of a grasp you have of those skills, the more easily and surely you'll play the role of sex educator.

TEN TIPS ON SEX TALKS

1. Begin at the beginning.   That holds true for both what to say and when to say it. "I think a child should have basic reproductive information before he reaches kindergarten," says Mrs. Lucile Cantoni of the Family Service of Metropolitan Detroit. She and a number of other experts feel, however, that the more explicitly sexual aspects of sex education should be saved for later, when the child is around eight or nine.

Before discussing sex with even the youngest child, you might find it helpful to review age-appropriate sex-education materials for yourself. If you're a typical parent you'll surprise yourself by what you discover you *don't* know, or have forgotten, about the physiology of sex. The more you know what you're talking about, the better prepared you are to discuss these matters with your child.

2. *Be natural.* That is, if you want your youngsters to adopt a natural, relaxed attitude toward sex. Don't be too cutesy about terms and phrases. There's nothing wrong with calling a penis a penis and a vagina a vagina—unless, of course, you think there's something wrong with the penis or the vagina. To call a sex organ "that" or "a little thing" or something of the sort one year, and something more to the point the next, when this little game isn't being played with other parts of the body, is to say, "I've singled this one out for special treatment." The youngster has to wonder why. And the youngster has a good point: Why?

3. *Take advantage of openings.* Should you wait for the child to ask sex questions? Or do you plunge right in one fine day with a splendidly researched and well-organized little lecture on reproduction? Neither. The key again is naturalness. Answer questions as they come up—and take advantage of situations that offer spontaneous, unforced openings.

Such openings aren't hard to find in everyday life. A kitten seen nursing, a pregnant woman passed on the street, a baby brother or sister being bathed, even an egg taken from the refrigerator—all can ease you into some comment on sex or nurture.

At the same time don't overdo it. It's hardly being natural about sex to seize on *every* suitable opportunity for a lecture on sex education. Not every occasion needs to be taken advantage of, not every day or every week needs to have time spent on parent-child sex talk.

4. *Keep within the child's limits.* Too much of a good thing

is as bad as too little. Maybe in response to parents who never talked sex to *them*, maybe because they're not really that much at ease with the subject, some mothers and fathers oversell sex. They become very scientific. They go into great physiological detail. I've heard of mothers who expose their five-year-old daughters to a lengthy discourse on menstruation and then go on to show them the tampons that absorb menstrual blood. The five-year-olds don't understand it all, but do know that all that talk about bleeding scares them.

"It's not wise to give an explanation for something before the child is ready or interested or can see the nature of it," counsels Dr. Stanley R. Lesser, a child psychiatrist. "It's at the other extreme from saying nothing at all."

Children have definite limits to toleration for sex talk, beyond which they feel bored, nervous, anxious, or threatened. Some are good at tuning out what they don't want to hear; others aren't. A child whose level of toleration has been exceeded usually shows it some way: by not responding, making noises, getting giddy, laughing too hard, suddenly being naughty, and the like. If you see any of those signs, it's high time to end the talk. In discussing things or answering questions, be simple, concise, direct—and encourage the child's response.

5. Talk on the child's level.   One mother told me how, when she and her seven-year-old son were baking a cake together, a remarkable thing happened: breaking one egg she discovered the embryo of a chicken inside. She seized on a chance to expand on that little miracle; she drew pictures showing how an egg is fertilized and then went on to explain that in human beings, too, an egg is fertilized. When she got all through, her little boy broke into a laugh and said, "Aw, Mom, next you'll be telling me human beings come in shells, too!"

This mother's instincts were right, but in one respect her approach was wrong. She'd forgotten who she was talking to. A preschooler and a seven-year-old are two different species. As you would with any other topic, try to gauge the child's level of comprehension and sophistication. If you talk above the children, you lose them. If you talk beneath children, they wonder what's wrong with you—in other words, you lose them.

So don't go blithely on with your little talk, oblivious to the fact that your child may be staring at you glassy-eyed from boredom or lack of comprehension. Make sure you're getting through.

6. *Be straightforward.* Don't sugar-coat or falsify information. To tell the preschooler he came from the stork, only to correct the myth at a later time, is both to say, "I lied to you," and, "There's something shameful about the truth." To tell the eight-year-old caught masturbating, "Pull your pants back up or you'll catch a draft" is to say something both of you know is phony. When children are consistently told untruths about sex you can hardly expect them to trust you later on when you want to talk straight.

As for masturbation, that troublesome issue: most parents these days don't tell their children they'll grow insane if they masturbate; but indirectly, by distracting them, they convey that the practice is wrong. But it isn't wrong at all; as every child guidance expert agrees, it's a perfectly normal practice. It's *inappropriate*, however, for a child to masturbate at such a time or place that others encounter him at it. But that, obviously, is a different issue.

Oscar Rabinowitz, director of group therapy for the Madeleine Borg Child Guidance Institute, advises: Let the child know that the practice isn't wrong but that the occasion is, that this is an act one performs in private. When such an explanation is followed by distraction—"Johnny, why don't you go out and play now?"—the distraction has another cast to it. You've given permission in general—but not for this specific, public moment.

7. *Be very clear.* Children do a lot of fantasizing about sex, that great unknown, and when things aren't made clear to them their fantasies tend to run away with them. A child who's

merely told, "You come from Mommy's tummy," often jumps to the conclusion that the baby actually is expelled from the mouth or the anus, which are the only two orifices he can imagine in this context. When Mother merely says, "Babies come from seeds (or eggs) inside their mommies' tummies," what children think of are the seeds they know, like watermelon seeds, or eggs like the kind they have for breakfast. Then they can't help wondering whether they, too, having swallowed seeds or eggs, will have babies.

In a report to doctors, Dr. Gerald Shipman of Wisconsin State University points out that adolescents sometimes have phobias about eating seeds or eggs; such phobias are related to these earlier fantasies. Better, Dr. Shipman suggests, for Mother to say, "The baby grows in a special place called the womb. It starts from a tiny egg cell so small you can't see it."

8. *Expect delayed reactions.* Don't assume that just because a child acts bored or asks no questions after you've made some comments about sex, nothing was absorbed. Children take in what they want to take in, but don't necessarily show at once that it has made an impression. You may wait expectantly for a reaction to your sex-education efforts—only to have that reaction come days or weeks later.

A mother who is also a social worker told me about having talked to her two boys about sex one day only to have them react with evident boredom. A few days later she was driving them to visit a friend when they suddenly popped up with all kinds of questions about how babies are born.

"It all seemed to come out of the blue," the mother says, "but it really went back to that talk we'd had. I had opened up the subject—and that enabled them to ask me the questions that were on their minds."

In other words, the mother's talk had given the youngsters *permission* to talk about sex on their own. That's an important point. When you talk about sex you're saying something beyond the immediate subject matter. You're also saying, "It's perfectly proper to think and talk about sex. My doing this with you means it's okay for you to do it with me, too."

9. *Don't get too personal—or too graphic.* If children want to know something about their parents' own sex lives, how should the parents respond? There are two points of view among the many mental-health experts I consulted. One faction says: Avoid being personal; make the child aware that some things are private; don't run the risk of creating a situation that's overstimulating for all concerned; answer questions about your own sex life as generally as possible—in fact, all such questions ought to be answered in the third person.

The other faction says: It's okay to be personal; you can talk to your children about everything, your own sex life included; to pretend you don't have sex is to negate the attitude that sex is healthy and normal; in any event, when youngsters find something too threatening they stop hearing it, they shut it off.

Which viewpoint is best? Rephrase that in light of your own family: "Which viewpoint suits us best?" Much depends on the particular family—how healthy it is, how well family members relate and communicate with each other, how free the home atmosphere is in terms of sex talk, whether the children are easily overstimulated.

You know your own situation and can make your own decision. Whichever it is, though, keep things light and casual. The experts on both sides of the fence agree that it's very poor practice to be graphic about your own sex lives. The more detail you go into the more you feed into the child's fantasies and encourage erotic feelings to surface. Sexy images have a definite place in children's lives, but when parents evoke them it creates emotional tensions that are very difficult for everyone involved to handle.

10. *Avoid sex-talk segregation.* Some parents make a point

of dividing the task of sex education very rigidly between them. Fathers talk only to sons, mothers only to daughters. This happens all the more so when children approach puberty.

You may feel it's more appropriate to talk about sex only with your same-sex child, and you may be much better prepared to do so. Mothers, for instance, can certainly talk about menstruation with more sureness and knowledge and understanding of the feelings involved than can fathers. But that doesn't mean it's the best thing for fathers to absent themselves where their daughters' sexuality is concerned, or for mothers never to talk sex with their sons.

If at all possible, play it loose. In some situations a sexually segregated talk may be best, may be what the child in fact wants. In other situations, both parents can pitch in. Many if not most sex educators these days would encourage joint participation for several sound reasons: whatever the topic, the opposite-sex parent presents a different perspective. Moreover, the opposite-sex parent can probably do a better job of clearing up myths and misconceptions the child may have in relation to that sex—and it's sound sex education to teach your children not only facts of life about their own bodies but about those of the opposite sex, too. (When they approach puberty, boys should certainly learn the facts about menstruation, girls about spermation.) Finally, when a child's male and female parents both talk freely about sex, that child learns an important lesson: it's all right for men and women to talk to each other freely, openly, without embarrassment about sex.

14

The Children: How to Understand Their Sex Talk

SEX AND NONSEX

Question: If it sounds sexy, is it sexy? Answer: Not necessarily. Yet, says Oscar Rabinowitz, parents often fall into this communications trap—they automatically assume that when their children say something that *sounds* sexy it must *be* sexy. Nothing could be further from the truth. What parents tend to do is to impose their own adult, narrowly sexual view of things upon their children's questions or remarks, while the children may have something quite different in mind.

It's not the greatest way to communicate with one's children. It confuses them. It subtly brainwashes them; pretty soon they, too, begin to see things from an exclusively sexual perspective even when there's only the faintest suggestion of sex. Most importantly, it doesn't get to the heart of *their* concerns. To keep that from happening, avoid taking your child's seemingly sex-related remarks or questions at face value. Instead, explore them. There may not be another meaning; everything may be right on the surface. On the other hand, the surface words may be covering up feelings or concerns the child won't or can't make obvious.

139

This kind of exploration isn't always easy to accomplish. You're a concerned parent, not a child psychologist with special training in the art of getting to children's hidden feelings. Nevertheless, with a little patience and sensitivity, you can usually bring out those beneath-the-surface concerns. Sometimes all it takes is a few judicious questions.

Let's see how it works out in three typical examples:

Bobby, a sprightly seven-year-old, asks his mother, "Where do I come from?"

Mom, who has been waiting for just this question, is fully prepared. She has read up on things and now does her stuff, going into a careful, brilliant exposition of what conception is all about. Everything is perfectly executed and when she finishes she can't help feeling a little proud of herself.

That's when Bobby looks at her wearily and says, "Mom, I didn't mean any of that stuff. I meant, where did we live before we moved here?"

A deflated Mom shakes her head wonderingly. She might have saved herself a lot of trouble by responding to the boy's question about where he came from with a little question of her own: "What do you mean, Bobby?"

Andrea, just four, has a somewhat similar question for her mother. She asks, "Where do babies come from?"

Now, Andrea's question doesn't seem in the least ambiguous, so her mother launches into a well-done sex talk. But it doesn't serve Andrea's needs any more than Bobby's mother's talk served his. Something has been puzzling and disturbing the little girl; she has gotten it into her head that babies are ejected from the bowels. So every time she has a bowel movement she thinks she's losing a little brother or sister. Her mother, of course, has no way of knowing that this is on her mind. But instead of taking Andrea's question at face value she could have made an effort to find out if there was anything behind it.

In that case the dialogue between daughter and mother would have started along these lines:

Andrea: Where do babies come from?

Mother: Andrea, where do *you* think babies come from?

This would have opened things up for the child. Either immediately or with a little encouragement she could have told her mother what she thought and had the disturbing misconception cleared up for her.

Patricia, a pert six-year-old, suddenly exclaims, "Mommy, I want to be big like you and have big breasts like you!"

It's the loaded word "breasts" that immediately registers with Mommy. She's startled. So she may hurriedly say the first thing that comes to her mind: "Well, you're too young to have breasts"—which is a put-down for the child, a reminder of how little and immature she is. Or the mother may say, "Oh, Pat, don't talk about such things!"—which Pat correctly interprets as, "You're bad for having said that." Or mother's reply may be, "Pat, dear, when you're old enough to have a baby you'll have breasts like Mommy's"—a heavily sexual remark that simply encourages the child's fantasies to run away with themselves.

A more helpful approach would be to take the time to find out what Pat really means and then to respond in kind:

Patricia: Mommy, I want to be big like you and have big breasts like you!

Mommy: That's nice, dear. Why would you like to have breasts like me?

Patricia: Because I'll be able to wear nice clothes like you and have a house like you and do what I want—just like you.

It's cleared up. What Patricia had in mind wasn't sexually oriented at all; it had to do with having a sense of power and accomplishment. Now Patricia's mother can answer appropriately.

Mommy: That's a good reason, Pat. Don't worry, you'll

grow up to be a big lady. You'll have your own clothes and things and take care of yourself.

In sum, when your child asks what seems like a sex question or makes a remark that seems sexually loaded:
—Don't hurry in with the first answer that comes to mind.
—Take time to explore the question or remark.
—Then, if you uncover any underlying concerns or misconceptions on the child's part, address yourself to them.

DIRTY WORDS

In every generation children have, after some slight exposure to the outside world, come home proudly displaying newly learned words, four letters and up. All the more so today, when what was formerly known as vulgarity has been gaining wide acceptance among all social classes, sexes, and ages, and those selfsame words are all around us, wherever we turn.

Despite their prevalence, most parents probably would still prefer their children not to use them—certainly not habitually and around the house—but aren't quite sure how to handle the situation. One reason they're not is that they concentrate on the particular word and its most obvious physiological meaning, rather than searching for the meaning the child might have attached to it. Children hardly ever use "dirty" words in an explicitly sexual context; even when they do want to convey something sexual in saying them, this is usually not their primary intent. But those words *are* a form of communication from child to parent.

Let's say six-year-old Gina, her second month of school behind her, accidentally unstrings some beads she was making into a bracelet and exclaims, loudly enough for her mother to hear her, "Oh, fuck!"

Gina's mother could turn beet-red, yell, threaten to wash the girl's mouth out with soap, and make her promise never to use that word again. Gina would be hurt, puzzled, angry; she would immediately catch on that this is a bad word to say, and if she wants to be bad, that's the word to say around her mother. Once she became aware of its sexual connotations she would also have had it reinforced in her mind that sex is bad.

On the other hand, Gina's mother could try to find out why her daughter used the word, and used it as loudly as she did.

Mother: Gina, that word you just used—where did you hear it?

Gina: In school. Some of the kids were using it.

Mother: How were they using it?

Gina: They were yelling it in the yard, and giggling a lot.

Mother: Were you yelling it now, dear, because you wanted me to explain it to you?

Gina nods. She had sensed that the word wasn't quite right and wanted to know what it meant, but didn't want to come right out and ask.

Mother: Well, it's a way of saying "sexual intercourse." Children—and sometimes grownups, too—use the word in a kind of silly, dirty way. But Gina, it's really not appropriate to use around the house—or to yell on the street, either.

In this more useful approach, Gina's mother doesn't make a big deal of things. She finds out why Gina used the word, gives her an explanation, and calmly tells her the conduct she prefers in relation to it. Not being threatened or made to feel guilty, Gina is apt to be much more willing to cooperate.

Sandy, who's seven, comes bounding into his house loudly exlaiming, "Dad, guess what—I fucked Alice after school today!"

Dad looks startled, can't help grinning, then says, "Son, I bet you're using that word without really knowing what it means."

"Sure I do," says Sandy, "I fucked Alice—had a big fight with her!"

Dad gently questions his son and what emerges is that

Sandy has somehow gotten the word "fuck" confused with "fight," assuming they both mean somewhat the same thing—probably because "fuck" is so often used in an aggressive way. Now Dad has a chance to explain the real meaning of the word, its various uses, and the question of its appropriateness.

David, who's a couple of years older, knows exactly what the word means but uses it a couple of times around his father one particular week.

David's father says, "David, I've talked to you about using the word fuck."

"Yeah, Dad, I forgot."

"You know, sometimes boys your age use the word to show off, to show how big they are." David doesn't reply and his father goes on, "But I just have the feeling that you're not trying to do that."

"Nope."

"All right, son. What are you so angry about?"

And then it comes out: David is still miffed because a week earlier his father had refused to raise his allowance.

Whereupon the father says, "You certainly have a right to your anger—but there are better ways of expressing it to me than the way you did."

So it goes. In most instances children use four-letter words mainly to discover their meaning, to test how much they can get away with, to tease, to provoke a parent, to show anger, to show off, to engage in a test of wills. Whatever the reason, a little patient questioning on the parent's part may be necessary before it emerges.

Even today most children don't make a habit of using swear words around their parents unless their parents don't care or frequently use the same words around their children. When boys and girls do persist in using words their parents would prefer them not to, it constitutes a communication all its own:

often the children involved feel themselves tremendously pressured at home, and by tyrannizing their parents in this manner they're getting back at parents who tyrannize them in other ways.

"I WANT TO MARRY YOU"

If you're a mother and you have a little boy, there comes a time when he pays you the highest tribute he can think of: "Mommy, I want to marry you!" If you're a father and you have a little girl she's similarly apt to show her feelings for you by saying, "Daddy, I want to marry you!"

You really don't have to be a Freudian to recognize the developmental nature of this childlike phase: children's fantasies first center on their cross-sex parents. That moment comes, that moment goes; while it's there it foreshadows the time, years later, when these children will be assuming their own adult heterosexual roles and relationships. But whatever erotic undercurrent may be present, this is also the child's way of saying how much he loves and admires and wants that parent, wants him for his very own.

It's an important communication on the child's part and there are positive and negative ways of handling it:

Parents sometimes laugh it off:
Steve: Mom, when I grow up I want to marry you.
Mom: (*laughing*): Isn't that cute?
This is a put-down. Here the child has been expressing some pretty strong feelings and the object of his affections is making light of them. This hurts; moreover, it doesn't help him deal with his fantasy of marrying Mom.

Parents sometimes overdramatize the situation:
Lisa: Daddy, when I grow up I want to marry you.

Daddy: You can't ever marry Daddy, honey. Daddy is already married to Mama and loves her very much.

So Daddy *is* married to Mama, but that's not reason to rub the child's nose in her fantasy. Daddy does that because her remark makes him uncomfortable: he senses sexual implications on some level, vague or otherwise, therefore feels he has to be forthright in rejecting the offer.

Yet there's a double message in what he says: "If Daddy *wasn't* married to Mama, and *didn't* love her so much . . . " The implication offers plenty of fantasy material for the little girl.

So does any response that encourages the child to think of herself as a surrogate wife to her father or the boy child to think of himself as a surrogate husband to his mother. Such encouragement is always very destructive to the child involved, who then finds it very difficult ever to break the unhealthy tie the parent has created.

The best way of handling things is to accept the child's remark in the context in which it's given:

Betsy: Daddy, when I grow up I want to marry you.

Daddy: I love you, too, Betsy, and when you grow up you're going to marry a nice man and be very happy.

And so she probably will if this is how her father always reacts to her. He has responded to her warmth and dealt realistically with her fantasy, and this is very reassuring to her.

Whether a talk consists of a simple exchange like this one, or of a prolonged discussion on any aspect of sex, the parents' task is always threefold: to respond to the youngsters' mood, to impart new information, and to correct their fantasies (if these need correcting). There's the essence of a successful parent-child sex talk.

15

The Teenagers:
Problems
and
Principles

WHY IT'S MORE DIFFICULT TO TALK

When Dr. Gerald Shipman questioned four hundred university students in Wisconsin about the kind of sex education they'd received at home, the usual pattern emerged. A low percentage of girls pronounced it adequate. Really little more than a handful of boys had anything positive to say about this aspect of their upbringing. And most significantly, even those boys and girls who praised their parents' efforts when they were children said there was a sharp drop in adequacy when they reached puberty and adolescence.

As those Wisconsin youths went, so goes the nation. Studies everywhere show that even if parents were adequate sex educators when their children were young, major communication blocks occur when the same children reach adolescence.

It's ironic—and sad. At puberty boys and girls undergo tremendous physiological and psychological changes; at adolescence they have to cope with the difficult social and emotional consequences of their burgeoning sexuality. These are the years when they have an urgent need to talk about sex—a need to

147

explore their feelings, air their fears, clear up misapprehensions, work out their values, come to some definition of right and wrong, test themselves against their family's standards and values. Yet this is precisely the time when parent-child sex talk often falters or breaks down completely.

The clearer you are about why the blocks occur, the more sensitivity and perception you can show, as the parents of a teenager, in trying to overcome them. They're usually not due to anybody's "fault" so much as they are in the nature of things between parent and adolescent:

—Your children are in turmoil now—scared and exhilarated by the sudden changes within them; wanting to be babied and taken care of as before, simultaneously wanting to break out of that childish dependency and strike out on their own. It's a turmoil that makes all significant parent-child communication more tense and difficult.

—The fact that they can perform sexually now is apt to make you more anxious and concerned. You worry about their welfare, about the potential for problems and trouble that suddenly exists both with sex and drugs.

—Their sexual awakening may reawaken somewhere within you the desires, worries, fears, anxieties, good scenes and bad that *you* experienced as an adolescent.

—In any event you're forced to confront their sexuality on a different, more mature, level than when they were children. Consequently you're forced to confront yourself and your own sexuality as you weren't before.

—That they've assumed their places as sexually functioning members of the family creates subtle changes in the way they and you relate—changes that are usually in the direction of greater modesty, privacy, and circumspection about sex.

—Such changes are related to a sexual reality that may make everyone concerned feel a bit embarrassed or guilty: on some level, parents can't help but be aware that their children are no longer children but sexually attractive young persons; the young persons themselves, especially around the early adolescent years, will almost surely have some fantasies centering on their opposite-sex parents. It's all perfectly normal but it does lead to self-consciousness.

While all these circumstances make parent-adolescent sex talk more difficult, they don't make it impossible. Patience, sensitivity, and a proper application of communications skills can help make it easier to talk.

NOT ALL PARENTS QUALIFY

The importance of good parent-adolescent sexual communications notwithstanding, nobody can legislate the ability to engage in it. No parent *must* engage in it. As is true with parents and younger children, some situations indicate a hands-off policy:

—When a parent (even one who was able to talk to his children when they were younger) finds himself acutely embarrassed or distressed in trying to handle a sex talk.

—When a parent has a clearly negative or fearful attitude about sex, considering it evil, dirty, a scourge of mankind, and so on, and doesn't want to inculcate his children with the same fear and negativism.

—When the marital relationship is fraught with serious sex problems, especially problems in which the adolescent is somehow involved.

In one such case, the wife—let's call her Maggie—began to have sexual fantasies about the new minister of the church she and her husband, Dave, attended. Though the minister didn't reciprocate her interest she went out of her way to cook, clean, and otherwise assist him. This infuriated Dave, all the more so when Maggie's sexual interest in him waned. In retaliation he became flirtatious with their fifteen-year-old daughter, which both aroused and repelled the girl and made her very hostile toward her mother. Under the circumstances, the few attempts Maggie and Dave made to counsel their daughter about sex ended in tears and recriminations.

Although this was an extreme instance it serves to illustrate the point: in some cases attempts at sex talk are apt to do more harm than good. If you feel you can't or shouldn't handle a sex talk with your adolescent child, perhaps the child's other parent is able to. Otherwise, encourage the young person to seek advice and guidance from an outsider who's trusted and respected— possibly another relative or family friend. A teacher, doctor, or clergyman might also be a good choice, depending on the individual—but that individual has to be someone the youth personally has confidence in.

The least helpful thing you can do if parent-adolescent sex talks don't seem feasible is to avoid the subject altogether, pretending the issue of sex doesn't exist. The young person's need for guidance and support won't go away and, even if he doesn't voice it, on some level he'll think you have failed him.

Some parents rationalize their unwillingness to talk: the less talk there is, the less the young person's curiosity is aroused; the less it is aroused, the less the likelihood of problems arising. This is a ridiculous rationale. When children are normal and healthy they *are* curious, they *will* be pressured sexually by their peer group and egged on by erotic messages in the mass media, they *will* be talking and probably experimenting with friends anyway. Under those circumstances, the more information they have, the better able they are to make choices and hopefully *not* get into trouble.

When parents are open and honest, when they admit that this is an area in which they can't be of real help, they're much more likely to gain their children's respect than if they say nothing. A college girl told me that when she reached puberty her mother informed her that she should be talking to her about sexual matters but couldn't. "I know I'll make a mess of things and that's not fair to you," the girl recalls her mother saying, "but I know you have a lot of things of your mind so let's sit down and think of who you'd be comfortable talking with." The girl was grateful for her mother's approach.

It takes a good deal of honesty and considerable strength of character to use the approach that mother did. But in one important respect—in the parental concern it shows—it's parent-adolescent sex talk at its best.

GETTING STARTED

If you've done a proper job of communicating with your children about sex up to the time they reach puberty, you're not really just "getting started." You're simply continuing this form of communication, mindful of the new pressures and problems in connection with it.

If you really haven't talked about sex before to any extent, and suddenly wake up to the fact that this is something you "ought" to do with your child, you may well have a hard time of it. Your adolescent children might be receptive, but a reaction of acute embarrassment, even hostility, is more likely. In the first place, there's no history of sex talk between you; suddenly beginning such talk is apt to seem abrupt and unnatural. In the second place, if you're suddenly wanting to talk sex out of a sense of duty, that's exactly what they'll pick up and resent; they want to feel you're showing genuine concern, not merely being dutiful. So don't be surprised, puzzled, or angry if your efforts are rebuffed. You might be able to breach resistance by candidly admitting you've been remiss, that this isn't an easy topic for you to talk about. Candor can be disarming when used with people of any age.

Whether or not you and the adolescent have done a lot of talking about sex in the past, the keynote again is naturalness. You could usher the young person formally into the living room, shut the door, and begin a lecture on premarital intercourse, contraception, or whatever else is on your mind. You *could* do that kind of thing but it isn't likely that you'll get very far. Adolescents even less than adults like to be lectured. They hate to be preached to.

If there's something you want to get across, try to work it into an appropriate situation. For instance, some television programs now touch on all kinds of adult sexual themes; a particular show might serve as a springboard for a few comments on what you believe or don't believe to be appropriate sexual conduct. Newspaper items, movies, events happening to friends or acquaintances, a child's comment about something that happened on a date—all can serve as springboards. Even if a real discussion doesn't ensue, you'll have communicated something of your own beliefs.

Sex-education books and pamphlets suitable to teenagers can also facilitate communication, especially with younger adolescents. Note that word *facilitate*; it's not the same as *taking the place of*. Unless you're absolutely tongue-tied about sex, don't use the materials as a substitute for yourself. It's one thing to give a boy or girl something to read and say, "You'll probably have some questions when you're finished reading; any time you want to talk, just tell me." It's quite another when the child comes with a question of his own and you say, "Well, now, let's see what Dr. So-and-So has to say about this." If your child has come to you he wants to know what *you* think—particularly if it involves standards, values, and issues that require a personal decision. He doesn't want you to cop out by using some stranger's advice in a book. Teenagers can read that stuff as well as you can.

Most of all, getting started on sex talks means dealing with the day-to-day practical problems that come up: addressing yourself to the concerns your child brings to you, deciding when dating is allowed to begin, fixing the when-you're-to-come-home-at-night time, setting limits on the extent and frequency of dating, the advisability of unchaperoned weekend trips ... These myriad situations bear directly or indirectly on the sex life of the adolescent and involve setting up sexual standards and offering parental guidance. They can also launch broader talks on aspects of sexuality that parents or teenagers are especially concerned about.

Young adolescents generally are very concerned about their own physical growth—the appearance of body hair, penis size, breast size, whether they're physically normal (this preoccupies boys), how their development compares to that of their peers, and so on. Soon enough, though, these concerns shift to social-sexual ones that have to do with dating, petting, mating, masturbation, and homosexual fantasies or experiences. There's plenty of material for talk.

CAUTIONS

By the time children reach adolescence, they're not likely to be overtly curious about their parents' sex lives; a kind of protective instinct born of the incest taboo takes over. In fact, many teenagers find it difficult to accept their parents as sexually functioning and responsive beings; it's easier, in terms of their fantasies, to make believe their parents are asexual. Some family-life experts feel that if a teenage boy or girl does ask many questions about his or her parents' sex life the child is being sexually overstimulated to a marked degree.

Extreme situations aside, the professional difference of opinion about whether it's good or bad for parents to refer to their own sexual activities remains. This, again, is something you'll have to resolve individually. Some families can handle such references easily and comfortably; others can't. But the points made in Chapter 13 still stick: if you do talk about yourselves, avoid being graphic or going into much detail. Thus, if an adolescent asks a parent about oral-genital sex and whether the parent has ever tried it, one reply might be, "Well, sure, it's perfectly normal." That's information. To go into all the nuances of how it's done and what it feels like—that's titillation.

Some modern mothers and fathers, resolved to put sexual repression to an end for *their* children, are very open and physical around them. They go beyond a playful slap on the rump to overt petting; some such parents also brag to their children about past or present love affairs. This can be disturbing to an adolescent because it triggers the very fantasies he'd like to submerge. What is more, this kind of parental exhibitionism has a competitive edge to it. As Dr. Lesser puts it, "It's not unusual for parents to try to have their children look at them as swingers." He adds that when parents endeavor to outdo their children sexually, the children may try to outdo them in the same way.

So much for the parents' sex lives; adolescents have their own, and here there is another difference of opinion among professionals. There are those who feel that parents should never listen to the intimate details of their children's sexual activities; that everything had best be discussed in the third person; that any problem requiring specific exploration of the young person's physical relationships ought to be left to persons other than the parents.

Needless to say, many other authorities find this view much too rigid. If the adolescent has so much confidence in his parents as to come to them with intimate problems, these experts hold, something good has been happening right along between them—and they should take advantage of it.

No professional concerned with the mental health of adolescents advocates being too inquisitive, though. Don't demand or even encourage lengthy accounts of the teenager's sexual activities—what goes on, how it feels, and so on. An unfortunate practice some parents engage in is to wait for their children to return home from a date, or accost them in the morning, and question them closely about what intimacies transpired. No matter how it is rationalized, this is an invasion of the adolescent's privacy; moreover, it provides a cheap thrill for the parent because it is a way of living through the child vicariously. The practice makes teenagers resentful and distrustful, and is very unhealthy for all concerned.

Prompted by their own repressive childhoods or by a wish to see their children popular, some parents pressure them to become sexually sophisticated. Such pressure is usually applied without regard to the child's own readiness for the activity, whatever it may be. One common way parents do this is to push their twelve- or thirteen-year-olds into dancing and dating. Another way it happens is for mothers to tell their fifteen- or sixteen-year-olds, "I'm going to get you some contraceptive pills; there's no telling what can happen."

If the child in the early teenage years doesn't want to date yet and is forced or shamed into doing so, the experience is likely to be a miserable one. It makes the child feel inadequate and may make him or her withdraw all the more. Of course, some children of pushy parents go the other way; in effect they say, "Okay, you want me to perform? I'll show you!"—and then run wild.

As for the sixteen-year-old presented with contraceptives, if sex wasn't on her mind at all she is likely to be shocked and dismayed, and make the interpretation, "Mother wants me to go ahead and do it." (Conversely, some mothers are afraid to help their daughters get contraceptives because it *is* a form of encouragement, but if a girl is in a sexually sophisticated crowd and wants the pill, but is flatly refused, she may work out her own revenge—pregnancy. Parents are on the spot, but they may be less so as increasing numbers of doctors and clinics provide for the contraceptive needs of teenage girls. It is one thing for a parent to hand a daughter a box of pills, so to speak; it's another to say, "I wish you'd wait but I can't stop you from getting contraceptives." In the second instance the parent expresses her standards, but is realistic about the girl's ultimate autonomy without giving in to it.)

If adolescents are to grow into mature adults, pushing them sexually is the worst way to accomplish it. Parents who apply this kind of pressure should be honest with themselves—they should recognize that they are doing so for their own gratification (using the child for things missed when they were young), rather than for the child's own good.

16

The Teenagers:
Applying
Communications
Skills

EXPLORING YOUR ADOLESCENT'S NEEDS

Teenagers no more than children always talk straight about sex. They may be hazy about what they want to ask or say, their emotionalism about their own sex lives may keep them from expressing what really concerns them, they may be wanting to test their parents as a way of sorting out their own thoughts. In other words, they often need help in defining and clarifying what's on their minds. Here are some suggestions and examples that may help you to help them:

Dig beneath the superficial question. Sally, just twelve, asks her mother, "What's a French kiss?" Sally's mother is surprised; she assumes the girl would know. Nevertheless she goes ahead and gives a fairly clinical explanation. That's it. Sally shrugs and says, "Okay, Mom." The girl's real questions haven't been answered. She *has* known right along what French kissing is. What she actually wanted to find out was something else: Is it enjoyable? Am I ready for it? If a boy wants to, do I have to?

When an adolescent asks for *general* information, sometimes that's all that's called for, but other times it masks a very specific *personal* concern. Instead of giving her explanation and

157

letting it go at that, Sally's mother might have said, "I wonder if there's something else you want to know about French kissing, something that has to do with you?" At which point Sally could have voiced her concern or otherwise showed that she wanted her mother to pursue the subject. One remark on the parent's part closes further communication, another invites it.

Explore the surface comment. Stephanie, in her second year of junior high school, tells her mother that her friend Doris is having sex with a boy in class. The mother immediately says, "Stephanie, you know I don't like you to gossip; what Doris does is her own business."

That's definitely closed communication. Stephanie's real concerns aren't being dealt with at all. A little probing would have helped the girl bring them to the surface: Should I stop seeing Doris? If I did something like that, what would you say? I'm torn between wanting to and not wanting to—what should I do?

If Stephanie's mother had instead immediately responded with, "Doris isn't a wholesome influence and I wish you'd keep away from her from now on," the result would have been the same. Superficially, Stephanie's questions would have been answered—but she'd have received no help in resolving her dilemma. Her mother's arbitrariness would have put her off. She would have resented being told what to do; resented, too, the attack on her friend and the lack of any attempt to find out how she personally felt about the event.

Here would have been a perfect opportunity for a heart-to-heart chat, an opportunity for the mother to help the girl plumb her emotions and at the same time get across her own convictions about the meaning of the sex act.

Don't jump to conclusions. You may think you know your teenagers so well you can already tell exactly what's going on underneath the surface—and that, therefore, you have no need to dig. But no matter how well you know your children, you can't be sure. It's very easy to assume we know exactly what someone else is thinking or feeling, especially someone close to us—only to have it turn out that these are *our* thoughts or feelings which we're merely attributing to the other person. This can have painful consequences, especially when the target is a sensitive teenager.

Daniel is such a boy. Daniel is a thirteen-year-old troubled by his lack of aggressiveness. He decides to talk to his mother about this and says, "Mom, the other guys act much tougher than I do. Is there something wrong with me?"

His mother thinks she knows exactly what's bothering him, so she immediately responds, "Don't worry, Daniel, you're not going to be a homosexual. Men can be sweet and kind, too."

Daniel has had something quite different in mind: he doesn't shove to get to the front of the line the way the other guys do, he doesn't feel like fighting back when a kid starts to push him around. Deep down he may have some worries about homosexuality, but it is not what he wanted to talk about; the fact that this is what his mother jumped upon, however, makes him think, "My God, I must be showing something—something must really be the matter with me." He becomes so anxious he finally winds up in a therapist's office, where he gains reassurance.

Clearly, Daniel's mother could have saved a lot of grief and trouble if, instead of jumping to conclusions, she'd checked Daniel out to see what was actually on his mind.

HOW SEX TALKS GO WRONG

In some families sex talk is unpredictable. Sometimes it works fine and other times it explodes into confusions, misunderstandings, arguments, hurt feelings, and other unpleasantnesses. If this happens in your family see if one or more of these causes apply:

The timing is off. Whether it's brief or protracted, sex talk does need attention from the participants. When it's attempted on the run—when Mom is late for the hairdresser, Dad is preoccupied with a business worry, the teenager is about to hurry off on a date—there's really no chance for a meaningful exchange. The result is that nothing gets accomplished or all kinds of misunderstandings occur. A talk works best when everybody involved is relaxed, has the time for it, and really wants to participate.

There are semantic difficulties. Many a blow-up is helped along by the fact that parents and adolescents *think* they're talking the same language when in fact they're not. The fad terms a teenager uses may leave a parent puzzled—or guessing wrong. Even a seemingly understandable term may have different connotations for each. Take "making out"—to a particular young person it may mean necking or petting; to a parent it may mean sexual intercourse. Probing the meaning of terms helps promote understanding.

The message is confused. Parents sometimes come across in a muddled way, maybe because they're not sure of what they're saying and don't want to admit it. Teenagers sometimes sound muddled, too—either because they haven't thought through the particular issue under discussion or because, underneath it all, they really don't want Mom or Dad to help them. If they're not being helped, after all, they can accuse their parents of being unhelpful. This is a fairly common form of adolescent rebellion, whether the issue revolves around sex or anything else. Ask the teenager if you're making yourself clear; if you aren't, reword your thoughts in more lucid terms. If you notice the teenager conveying confusion, request a clarification. All of you have to be as clear as you can about what you want to say if you really want to get anything accomplished.

The words are provocative. Provocative means the parent goads the adolescent; the adolescent goads the parent; each says things in a way that inflames the other. However it works out, it doesn't work. Talking ends in fighting. On a conscious level maybe nobody wants this to happen, but there are reasons why one or both are being inflammatory. Fighting is a way of dodging issues. Fighting is a way of fulfilling a prophecy: "See, one can't talk to you in a civilized manner," or, "See, you don't really understand me." This isn't an easy pattern to break. If you consider the matter carefully and suspect that maybe you're being provocative, there's no substitute for trying very hard to stop. If, on the other hand, you feel you're the target for provocation, make a real effort not to let yourself be provoked; provokers usually don't go on provoking very much when there's no fun in it.

The attitudes are inflexible. When parent and teenager both start off with the assumption, "I'm right, period," the message they immediately convey to each other is, "You're wrong, period." That approach is almost sure to bring on hostility. Hostility keeps them from listening to each other and the outcome is exactly what both expect: an impasse and an even greater conviction on the part of each that "I'm right." Unless one of you is willing to break out of the pattern and start talking feelingly, start listening and checking each other out, that pattern will go on indefinitely. Since you're older, wiser, and not caught in the confusions and turmoils of adolescence, the honor logically falls to you.

Somebody is sending a double message. If you think you're saying one thing and the teenager actually does the opposite, you may, without realizing it, be engaging in some sexual double-talk. Mothers sometimes say to their daughters, "Be good, be obedient, don't become sexually involved"—but also convey, "Be popular, be sexy, have all the fun I missed out on." Fathers sometimes tell their sons, "Sow your wild oats, have your fling, then marry and settle down and be happy"—but also convey, "Watch out for women, they'll drain you dry, get them before they get you." Parents who constantly accuse their children of misbehaving sexually are in effect saying, "It's irresistible—go ahead and do it." If your son or daughter seems confused by what you say, or behaves contrariwise, try to step back and see if you're sending out conflicting messages. You have nothing to lose but the wrong half of the message.

There's much generalized discomfort. It may be that the very act of talking sex is a disturbing one to you or to the teenager. If you can all sit down and talk together about the *problem* of talking about sex, as distinct from talking about a sexual issue itself, you may find your reserves melting down. By metacommunicating, by talking about talking, you're working out your own discomfort and also helping the adolescent shed his or hers.

GUIDANCE AND DECISION-MAKING

When children are quite young, parental decision-making is easy: parents know the world and its dangers, the child doesn't and can't reason, so a flat no is enough. As a child grows older and can begin to comprehend the differences between right and wrong, between safety and danger, the parental approach shifts: instead of a simple prohibition, it goes, "You better not do this because the consequences are such-and-such." As the child gains maturity there's a subtle change to "I wouldn't if I were you because the consequences may be . . . " By the time the child is well into the teens, parental decision-making has largely evolved to "Make your own judgments, but recognize what the consequences are."

This, at any rate, is the realistic, practical approach and it seems to work well in most areas of living. Sex is something else again. It is around decision-making that parent-adolescent sexual communication often becomes the most troubling. When the child asks for permission to do something that bears directly or indirectly on sex, it is then that tension and conflict are most apt to occur.

This isn't an easy time for parents. If you have adolescent children you know you're caught in all sorts of binds:

—You want the best for your children but you may not be sure what "best" is, since sexual values and behavior have been undergoing such drastic changes.

—You are aware that your children are under tremendous pressure from their peers to have sex and/or to do things that are sexually oriented; moreover, the pressure of "All the kids are doing it" can be an enormous one for parents.

—You no longer have the authority and control you did when your children were younger; you know that even if you turns thumbs down on something, they aren't bound by your decision; they're old enough now to go counter to your wishes either overtly or covertly.

—You want to rely on your children's good judgment but you're not altogether sure how good that judgment is as yet; you want to provide guidance but you aren't sure how much or when to give it.

There is no single magic solution for these dilemmas; to some extent you have to live with them. But the better you and the adolescent communicate, the less friction and the more understanding there is apt to be. There are ways of enhancing or diminishing that communication in the context of guidance and decision-making:

Don't merely give an arbitrary turn-down if adolescents come to you with a request you disapprove of. They will react to arbitrariness with anger. It is also an excellent way of getting them to defy you.

Don't go to the other extreme and say, "It's up to you. You'll have to decide." When teenagers come to you it means they *want* to hear what you have to say. Your refusal to commit yourself will seem like a copout—which it is. Furthermore, it will leave them feeling bewildered and with a sense of loss: you let them down.

Don't offer guidance without first having investigated your own sexual attitudes and values to see how valid, how honest, they are today. To base guidance and decision-making on "Well, this is the way we did it when I was young" is to look at the issue in terms of yourself rather than of the young people and their world.

Don't pretend to be sure of yourself and your values if you are really not, because you won't fool perceptive adolescents, you'll just lose them. Confusion and bewilderment are understandable today; much better to be honest and candid about it. Much better to say, "You know, this is something I was brought up to believe, and I live this way, and for me it's good, but I don't know if it will work for you or not," than to pretend you have all the answers when you don't.

Don't, by the same token, pretend to a set of beliefs when your personal life clearly contradicts them. The parents whose own sex lives are miserable, for instance, seem faintly ridiculous if they extol sex as something blissful and ecstatic. So does the mother or father who counsels premarital chastity or "only with someone you truly love"—but herself or himself has casual affairs. Your child will correctly interpret this approach for what it is—hypocritical. Better to say nothing, or to be forthright, or to refer the adolescent to a helpful outsider, as the occasion befits. The more hypocritical parents are, the more influence the adolescent's peer group will have; conversely, the straighter parents are, the greater the impression they are apt to make on their children.

Do try your utmost to use the confrontation technique, to bring on a heartfelt exchange of attitudes and feelings. Such an exchange can sometimes work little miracles, aside from the warmth and intimacy that is generated by the very act of engaging in them. Batting things back and forth can help you crystallize your own attitudes. Taking pains to explore your children's feelings can sometimes point the way to solutions in the face of difficult situations. On closer inspection things aren't always what they seem: just as an adolescent's comment or question can have something in back of it, so too can a request for permission. On the surface it may sound like, "I really want you to let me"—yet underneath, the teenager may be seething with ambivalence.

Take Janie, a fifteen-year-old. She tells her parents, "Some of the kids are going to spend the weekend at Jack's father's house on the beach. No grownups, just kids. I've been invited. Can I go?"

Janie's parents are unsure of what to do. Their first impulse it to say no; even though a lot of teenagers are going on unchaperoned trips together, these parents don't approve of it. But instead of giving a peremptory no, they wisely discuss the pros and cons with Janie, helping her explore her attitudes and also working out their own. After a while it becomes clear that Janie herself doesn't really feel she is ready to handle that kind of weekend, but has a hard time admitting that to herself, much less to the other kids. Her parents finally help her to see it is best she not go. This gives her the out she needs; their veto saves her from having to cope with a situation she finds uncomfortable and allows her to save face with her friends.

It may help you to know that, as a general rule, when adolescents show ambivalence they're really saying, "I would like to but I don't think I'm emotionally ready to cope with it"—and that holds true whether the teenager is considering an unchaperoned boy-girl weekend, or having sex for the first time, or whatever.

It may help you to know that boys and girls up to their mid-teens may scream to high heaven about *any* limits that parents set on their activities, but feel resentful when they're allowed to go their own way; this they interpret as "You don't care what happens to me."

Thus there are times when you'll have to say no even when you discern no ambivalence; you'll have to decide no—after talking things over—just because you feel the child isn't ready for the activity. As Dr. Eleanor B. Luckey, a specialist in child development at the University of Connecticut, puts it, "If we're close to our children we can judge pretty accurately the amount of responsibility they can take, and we must really avoid their taking responsibility which they can't assume. The consequences are too disastrous."

It is a tricky tightrope walk between too much permissiveness and too much restrictiveness, but every parent should do his best to walk it; children who show the most pathology, children who are the most unstable sexually, are those with parents who go to either extreme.

There will come the time—probably when your children are in their late teens—when you'll leave the final decision up to them—not as a copout from parental decision-making but because they have reached an appropriate level of maturity. But even then, if communication between you has been good and you enjoy mutual trust, what *you* have to say—your views, your opinions, your preferences, the pros and cons as you see them— will carry considerable weight. That's the ultimate in successful parent-adolescent sex talk.

17

Relatives, Friends, and Professionals

RELATIONS—AND SEXUAL RELATIONS

When children grow up and leave the family nest their parents usually make a little speech, the gist of which is, "If you have any problems, we're always here to help." But what happens when a sexual problem comes up? Many mental-health professionals have serious reservations about adults going to their parents for help with sex problems.

The nature of the parent-child relationship and the generational differences involved are at the heart of the professionals' objections. Many difficult feelings surface when adults come to their parents with sexual concerns. The adults may be torn between wanting to maintain independence from the parents and desiring to be dependent again. The emotional involvement may make it hard for parents to give calm, objective advice. The parent may have a sense of failure about a child with serious problems. There are apt to be resentments left over from the stormy adolescent years ("If you'd only listened to me then you wouldn't be in this pickle now"). There is the distinct possibility that the child's sexual problems will reactivate or intensify the parent's anxieties about sex. There is very apt to

167

be a renewed attempt on the part of the older generation to impose its values on the younger, which of course applies not only to parents but to other older relatives.

All kinds of complications can result, as they did in the case of a young woman named Donna. Married almost a year, Donna was markedly unsatisfied with her sex life. Her husband was a crude lover, giving little time to foreplay and leaving her teetering on the edge of orgasms she could never reach. One day, near tears, she asked her mother how to handle the situation. Donna's mother was outraged by her son-in-law's behavior. From that day on she worked and worked on Donna to get rid of him. Finally the young woman did separate from her husband.

Only later, through the intervention of a marriage counselor, did Donna come to understand that in a way her mother had victimized her. For all of her married life Donna's mother also had been sexually unfulfilled; her resentment against her own husband in particular and men in general was enormous. But somehow she could never bring herself to do anything about her own situation. In getting Donna to break with her spouse the mother was certainly, on a conscious level, acting with the best of intentions. But underneath this breakup was a realization of the fantasies the mother had had all these years about leaving her own mate.

Many professional counselors are also leery of brothers and sisters seeking each other's help with respect to sex problems. Generational differences are usually absent where siblings are concerned, but other complications present themselves. With same-sex siblings an element of rivalry can easily come into play. With cross-sex siblings intimate sex talk can also reawaken an attraction between them that may have existed in adolescent days. Such feelings cloud one's view of issues and affect the quality of advice that is given.

Undoubtedly there are people who benefit greatly from the help that parents or other close relations give them. But the general rule of thumb is: The closer the relatives are, no matter how concerned or well-meaning, the riskier it is to seek their advice for sexual problems; the more distant the relative, the greater the chance that the advice will be more sensible and objective.

FRIENDLY SEX TALK

People are probably much more prone to speak to friends than to relatives about sexual matters—all the more so when, as adolescents, they did little talking about it with relatives. Even when communication is good, many people instinctively realize the hazards involved and as adults avoid the practice.

As for friends, the nature and extent of our sex talk with them is an individual matter, of course; to a great degree it depends on individual definitions of privacy. There are persons for whom any but the most superficial sex talk even with the closest friends would violate their norms of privacy. But I suspect that most of us do share a lot of our sexual selves with friends, all the more so these days when the popularity of therapy, encounter groups, sensitivity sessions, and the like, as well as the candidness with which sex is treated in the mass media, influence openness about the subject.

When friends talk about sex, they talk about it either in general or in the context of a specific problem.

Talking about sex in general means sharing *feelings* about sex—much as we share feelings about food, liquor, politics, children, or whatever. It is the sharing of feelings of all kinds that breaks down isolation and builds a sense of communion—in other words, that makes friendship as rewarding a phenomenon as it is. Just as we don't share feelings about everything with every friend, so we don't share sexual feelings with everyone; and there are, of course, those men and women who place sex in a very special category and say nothing at all about it to anyone. But the more usual pattern is, the greater we trust a friend, the more the sharing occurs.

Sharing does more than enhance the spirit of community between ourselves and our friends; it is informative, too. It makes us realize we're not unique and alone; other people have the same wishes, fears, and assorted stray thoughts about sex buzzing through their heads that we do. We are comforted to know we're not alone.

Some friends go beyond the sharing of feelings. They exchange specific information on their own particular techniques, positions, and experiences. In part it is the equivalent of reading a sex manual. In part it is titillating. Offensive to some, it is rewarding to others.

If you "tell all" about what you do sexually with a boy friend, girl friend, or spouse, though, without the sexual partner you're referring to either present or aware of your disclosures, you are violating the intimacy between you.

In any event, don't make the sometimes serious mistake of measuring your own sexual functioning (or your partner's) against a friend's. There are people who compare themselves or their partners with friends and then feel they or their partners don't measure up. Friends sometimes tell tall tales about their sex experiences. Even when the account is truthful, it is unrealistic to measure yourselves against other people. By the same token, if somebody else describes a particular sexual technique and you try it and it doesn't work for you, don't be disheartened. Make room for individual differences; you in turn may well be enjoying things your friend doesn't.

Friends in similar sexual straits sometimes huddle together for comfort and support. I know several women, for instance, who often get together to talk about their respective extramarital adventures. Sharing such confidences is a way of working out the guilt they feel; again, it is tremendously supportive to realize, "I'm not alone." But this can be a double-edged sword; in some cases it can keep them from attempting to solve relationship problems that need working on.

As for out-and-out sex problems, getting advice from friends is by no means without risk. First of all, know your friend—be clear in your own mind that this is someone you can trust, that you can reveal the problem without fear of recrimination or of having your words held against you later on. Remember that revealing a problem is exposing yourself—and that once words are uttered you can't call them back.

No matter how close the friend, it's not that good an idea to reveal details of a mate's extramarital carryings-on. It's too much of a temptation. Many a husband's best friend, especially, has succumbed to it, trying to seduce the husband's wife upon learning that she is already playing around.

Beyond such strictures, bear in mind that friends, like relatives, are emotionally involved with you. They, too, may have their own unresolved sexual conflicts, and there may be an element of rivalry to your relationship. Also, they aren't trained to deal with sex problems. Any of these factors can blur objectivity and sensitivity, and render the advice suspect.

For all of these reasons it's best to approach friends with the basic assumption that they can't solve our sexual problems for us. What they can do is offer a perspective different from our own. They can offer support, reassurance, and understanding. Sometimes this is all we need to help us solve the problem ourselves. Sometimes this can give us the strength to bring the problem, if it's serious enough or bothers us enough, to a competent professional who *is* trained and *can* be objective.

TALKING TO PROFESSIONALS

When you go to a doctor, therapist, psychiatrist, or marriage counselor with a sex problem, it's only reasonable to expect this professional to ask you a number of personal questions about your sex life. Nevertheless, some people are taken aback at the very intimate nature of the questions that are sometimes directed at them. Depending on the professional and/or the nature of

the problem, you may be asked about your patterns of masturbation, what kinds of sexual positions and techniques you
engage in, how often you have sexual intercourse, whether you
engage in oral-genital sex, and a host of other intimate things
having to do with your sexual functioning.

The deeper the probe, the more inhibited you're likely to
be. An important part of the professional's job is to establish
trust, to make you feel at ease, and to create a helping rather
than a judgmental atmosphere. To the extent that he or she can
accomplish this, you will feel relaxed about revealing yourself.
Yet the professional can't do it all. Unless you do open up
sooner or later, there's no getting at the core of the difficulty. It
helps to remember that plenty of people have sat in that chair
or lain on that couch before you—and talked about the most far
out and bizarre aspects of themselves, probably much more far
out and bizarre than anything you will come up with. It helps
to remember that no sex problem is unique and no thought or
fantasy is one countless other people haven't thought or fantasized. You're definitely not alone.

Don't make the error of trying to please the counselor by
saying what you think he or she wants to hear; say what is on
your mind. Don't speak in the language you think is appropriate
to the occasion; speak in the language you feel most comfortable
using, whether that happens to involve the use of four-letter
words, clinical terms, or expressions in the vernacular. If the
professional says "premature ejaculation," for instance, and it
suits you best to say "coming too fast," by all means stick to
your pattern, not to his.

Though many people go to physicians for help with sex
problems, it seems that generally people feel more inhibited
talking to physicians than to mental-health people, most likely
because the mental-health people are more closely identified
with such problems. It is not uncommon for people to go to
their doctors with all kinds of nonsexual complaints for which

they have themselves checked out before getting to the real point, a sexual difficulty.

Doctors themselves are much more inhibited about sex than are mental-health clinicians, and many are sadly lacking the know-how it takes to treat sex problems. Incredibly, only in recent years, and largely through the efforts of Dr. Harold Lief (now director of the Marriage Council of Philadelphia) have medical schools begun to institute courses in human sexuality.

You should also know that significant numbers of doctors find it very hard to be nonjudgmental about sexual problems and patterns. Drs. Ira B. Pauly and Steven G. Goldstein of Oregon State University surveyed a substantial number of their colleagues and found that only about a third really felt at ease about the acceptability of premarital sex. Little more than half could flatly state that their religious beliefs "never" affected their medical treatment of patients with sex problems. Just barely over half claimed that their own attitudes about homosexuality "seldom" or "never" affected their treatment of male homosexuals.

You have every right to expect your doctor to be competent and nonjudgmental in the handling of sex problems—or to refer you to someone who is. There are doctors who do take the initiative and, acting in a professional manner, suggest such referrals. There are also doctors who try to bluff it through. The doctor who tries to bluff and doesn't really address himself to your sex problem shows it in several ways. Such a doctor:

—Is obviously uncomfortable or flustered in talking about sex.

—Seems to be in a hurry to get the conversation over with.

—Keeps trying to shift the subject from sex or from the emotional issues connected with the sexual problem.

—Goes into banal generalizations, as did an internist who told a patient complaining of frigidity, "A lot of women are like that—my wife's like that."

—Becomes heartily supportive, tending to laugh off the whole thing as nothing really to worry about.

—Is always ready with a pill, a tranquilizer, a kind of placebo—"Take two aspirins and call me in the morning"—as an answer to sexual distress.

If your doctor displays one or more of these signs, it is best you go to someone else for help, because you're not going to get it from him. If you suspect in advance that your doctor, great as he may be in his own area of specialization, isn't really equipped to deal with your sex problem, you may still want him to refer you to someone who is. A tactful way of handling the situation is to say, "Doctor, I have an emotional problem; perhaps you could suggest someone for me to see." More than likely he will breathe a sigh of relief and refer you to the best man or woman he knows in the proper field.

As for mental-health professionals, presumably they are trained to deal with sexual problems and to handle the language of sex without flinching. Nevertheless, not all such practitioners are that well trained either, or relaxed enough about sex to do a good job of communicating sexually with you. A survey of family-service social workers undertaken in the mid-1960s, for instance, shows that relatively few of those surveyed felt comfortable in focusing on sex problems directly, and some even hesitated to deal with sex problems at all. Before going into treatment, discuss the nature of the problem with the professional and find out whether he or she has had experience in treating similar cases.

Beyond such considerations, communication can succeed only if there's rapport between the two of you. No matter how good a therapist or social worker may be, that social worker or therapist may not be right for you. The one who is right will:

—Try hard to put you at your ease.

—Be warm and accepting.

—Give you a feeling of trust and confidence.

—Feel comfortable in talking about sex—and therefore make you feel comfortable in talking about it.

—Exhibit concern both for the physical problem and the concomitant emotional aspects.

Unless the professional shows these traits you will have a hard time opening up; in that case it may, again, be best for you to seek help from someone else. It is your problem—which gives you the right and makes it your responsibility to see to it that you have good "working" conditions.

18

Conclusion:
On Being a
Good Sexual
Communicator

ASSUMPTIONS

Talking sex—really talking sex feelingly and directly—can be frightening for anyone who isn't used to it. Like anything else, it becomes less awesome with exposure and experience. But don't rush things, or expect the miracle of openness to occur overnight. Whether you're talking with a spouse, lover, child, or professional, you will do better if you don't disregard feelings of anxiety or signs of reluctance, your own or the other person's. If somebody *is* feeling anxious or uncomfortable, drop the attempt for the moment. Avoid forcing the issue. There is always another day.

The key to successful communication can be summed up in a one-liner: *Don't act on the basis of assumptions.* Don't assume you know the meaning behind a child's seemingly sexual remark. Don't assume ahead of time your partner will veto that far-out technique you would like to try; it could be that your partner is just as interested as you are in trying it, but also just as hesitant about broaching the subject. Don't assume your partner will be revolted if you ask to have some special little quirk of yours satisfied; your partner may be happy to do it.

One husband I was told about wanted his wife to touch a finger to his anus while they had intercourse; this was a place of special sensitivity for him. But somehow he couldn't ask; he assumed she'd be disgusted if he did. Years later, after months of therapy, he finally got up the courage to ask her. Her reaction was, "Sure, why didn't you say so before?"

And don't assume, as so many people do, that you had better avoid bringing up a disagreeable issue because your partner wouldn't be able to take it. This point is made most vigorously at the Family and Children's Service's communications workshop in Minneapolis. Often people hold back saying unpleasant things that need to be said because of their assumption that the other party will somehow fall apart. Yet the end result of holding back on things that should be said often is the very result they fear: *less* closeness, *less* intimacy, a buildup of resentment and anger. Talking straight certainly is risky; I've stressed that many times. You don't know and can't guess your partner's reaction—it might be a hurt, angry, explosive reaction. Nevertheless, it is a serious error to assume people actually shatter so easily and therefore to hold back; we are, most of us, tougher inside than we give ourselves or others credit for.

Of course, if you are going to say something that is bound to be hurtful in some way, then you should examine your own motivations very carefully beforehand. Make sure before you open up that it is not a wish to hurt your partner, rather than a wish to resolve a troublesome situation, that's prompting you to speak. Having satisfied yourself on that score, proceed to weave an atmosphere that's as open and confronting as you can make it.

EXPECTATIONS

When you assume beforehand what your partner's reaction is going to be, rather than giving your partner a chance to express it directly, you're doing all the communicating for both of you. In effect, you're taking as much responsibility for your partner's communication as if you were literally doing all the talking for both of you.

This is contrary to open, effective exchanges—to real communication. When communication really is open and effective, responsibility bounces back and forth like a Ping-Pong ball. You take responsibility only for what you say and how you react. Your partner takes responsibility only for what he says and how he reacts. Then it's back to you for your reaction and your talk, And so forth.

From this arise other implications. The effective communicator knows he has no right to *expect* a specific reaction to something he asks or says. To expect a specific reaction as if it were one's due is once again, to put words into the other's mouth—to assume responsibility for him. Similarly, you need not and should not feel bound by the expectations the other person has for you, by the way you sense he *wants* you to react. It is certainly his prerogative to hope you will react in a certain way, but whether or not you will is wholly your prerogative, your decision. Your responsibility. The effective communicator doesn't impose—or feel imposed upon.

The ability to listen is another quality demanded of the effective communicator. An awareness that you don't have to feel imposed upon or under obligation simply because somebody asks or says something can make you into a better listener. Many people don't really listen to each other because they don't want to hear. And they don't want to hear because they don't want to feel they have to respond that certain way, the way that's expected of them. But the trap really is of their own making; they do, after all, have the right to free choice. Listening doesn't preclude free choice, doesn't imply submission or imposition. Listening simply means hearing the other person and then reacting as we see fit—be that "yes," "no," or "let me think about it."

The logical extension of "If I really hear then I have to submit" is "I have to submit in order to please the other person, in order to make him happy." The quest for happiness in general and sexual happiness in particular is fairly common in our American society. The mass media, especially the popular sex and marriage manuals, have had a great deal to do with this. Along with the positive results of making sex more acceptable and expanding our sexual knowledge they have also distorted reality.

As Marilyn A. Fithian, co-director of the Center for Marital and Sexual Studies, puts it, "The media help feed the unrealistic notion that if it's good today it's got to be better tomorrow. Some couples get to have a sexual philosophy that's akin to keeping up with the Joneses rather than being satisfied with what they have."

A single-minded quest for sexual happiness has a corrosive effect. It augments the feeling in people that they are under obligation to do things they may not want to do. It helps bring to sex the elements of duty, obligation, and competition. Moreover, as psychotherapist Oscar Rabinowitz observes, "When people expect too much of sex—of themselves and of each other in the sexual situation—it leads to disappointment. And this disappointment leads to anger."

The result is a reduction rather than an enhancement of sexual pleasure; eventually, some people are unable to perform at all. Conversely, by not seeking sexual happiness with the fervor of a religionist seeking the Holy Grail, you give yourself the best chance of finding it.

CHOICE

All of a person's attitudes about sex reflect that particular person's sexual values. But sexual values don't exist in a vacuum. We tend to operate with a kind of internal consistency in and out of bed: basically passive persons are most likely to show passivity in their sexual encounters; loving, giving people are usually the same way in their sexual relationships; and so forth.

This makes it apparent that we can't really separate sexual values from human values. Sex and humanity are of a piece. This has an import in terms of communication because it again extends the concept of choice in our talk, our responses, and our concrete actions. If we are being pressured to react sexually in a certain way and are undecided about what to do, we can sometimes change the narrow sexual problem into a more broadly human one and thereby expand our range of choices.

For example, a teenage girl who is still a virgin is being pushed by her boy friend to sleep with him. She is torn, doesn't know what to do. She could change "Should I or shouldn't I?" to "What do I want from sex right now in terms of myself as a human being? What kinds of relationships do I want with people? Do isolated sexual experiences fit into that framework? How do my views on sex and love fit in here?"

Similarly, other sexual questions can be viewed from a wider dimension with ourselves as human rather than strictly sexual beings at the center. This can help put us more in touch with ourselves, provide more options for us, and accentuate the feeling of "I have a right to make a choice."

Whether we are talking to ourselves or to others, having and allowing choice always leads to more open communication; compulsion always closes it off. What's more, choice always puts us at the center of things because along with the responsibility for making a choice comes the responsibility for communicating it—for saying, in effect, "Look, this is how I feel, this is the way I am." And there is no more open and effective communication than the kind that has us all in there as fully involved and expressing participants.

Good talk and good luck.

BIBLIOGRAPHY AND SELECTED READINGS

Berne, Eric. *Games People Play.* New York: Grove Press, Inc., 1964.

Berne, Eric. *Sex in Human Loving.* New York: Simon & Schuster, Inc., 1970.

Boylan, Richard B. *Infidelity.* Englewood Cliffs, N.J.: Prentice-Hall, Inc., 1971.

Brenton, Myron. *The American Male.* New York: Coward McCann, Inc., 1966.

Fast, Julius. *Body Language.* New York: M. Evans & Co., 1970.

Hall, Edward T. *The Silent Language.* Garden City, N.Y.: Doubleday & Co., 1959.

Gagnon, John H. "Sexuality and Sexual Learning in the Child." *Psychiatry* (August, 1965).

Goffman, E. *Presentation of Self in Everyday Life.* Garden City, N.Y.: Anchor Books, 1959.

Goldberg, Martin. "What Is The Psychological Significance of Various Coital Positions." *Medical Aspects of Human Sexuality* (February 1971).

Gunther, Bernard. *Sense Relaxation: Below Your Mind.* New York: The Macmillan Co., 1968.

Halleck, Seymour L. "Sex and Power." *Medical Aspects of Human Sexuality* (October 1969).

Heyder, D.W. and Wambach, H.S. "Sexuality and Affect in Frogmen." *Archives of General Psychiatry* (September 1964).

Hunt, Morton. *The Affair.* New York: The World Publishing Co., 1969.

Kinsey, Alfred C. et al. *Sexual Behavior in the Human Female.* Philadelphia: W.B. Saunders Company, 1953.

Klemer, Richard H. "Talking With Patients About Sexual Problems," in *Counseling in Marital and Sexual Problems: A Physician's Handbook.* Baltimore: Williams & Wilkins Co., 1965.

Lederer, Wm. J. and Jackson, Don D. *The Mirages of Marriage.* New York: W.W. Norton & Co., Inc., 1968.

Lorand, Rhoda L. *Love, Sex and the Teenager.* New York: The Macmillan Co., 1965.

Maslow, A.H. *Motivation and Personality.* New York: Harper & Row, 1954.

Mudd, Emily H., et al. *Marriage Counseling: A Casebook.* New York: Association Press, 1958.

Neubeck, Gerhard, ed. *The Extramarital Sexual Relations.* Englewood Cliffs, N.J.: Prentice-Hall, Inc., 1970.

Pauly, Ira B. and Goldstein, Steven G. "Physicians' Attitudes in Treating Male Homosexuals." *Medical Aspects of Human Sexuality* (December 1970).

Pauly, Ira B. and Goldstein, Steven G. "Physicians' Attitudes Toward Premarital and Extramarital Intercourse." *Medical Aspects of Human Sexuality* (January 1971).

Rubin, Isadore and Kirkendall, Lester A. *Sex in the Adolescent Years.* New York: Association Press, 1968.

Rubin, Isadore and Kirkendall, Lester A. *Sex in the Childhood Years.* New York: Association Press, 1970.

Scheflen, Albert E. "Quasi-Courtship Behavior in Psychotherapy." *Psychiatry* (Vol. 28, 1965).

Shipman, Gordon. "Sex Education Between Parent and Child." *Medical Aspects of Human Sexuality* (May 1971).

Shipman, Gordon. "The Psychodynamics of Sex Education." *The Family Coordinator* (January 1968).

Shulman, Bernard H. "The Uses and Abuses of Sex." *Medical Aspects of Human Sexuality* (September 1968).

Smith, Henry Clay. *Sensitivity to People.* New York: McGraw-Hill Book Co., 1966.

Walsh, Robert H. "The Generation Gap in Sexual Beliefs." *Sexual Behavior* (January 1972).